D1314331

THE CONVERGENT CENTURY

The Unification of Science in the Nineteenth Century

The Life of Science Library 46

BY HAROLD I. SHARLIN

The
Convergent
Century

The Unification of Science

in the

Nineteenth Century

ABELARD-SCHUMAN
London New York Toronto

© Copyright 1966 by Harold I. Sharlin

Library of Congress Catalog Card Number: 65-24773

First Published in Great Britain in 1967

LONDON | NEW YORK | TORONTO
Abelard-Schuman | Abelard-Schuman | Abelard-Schuman
Limited | Limited | Canada Limited
8 King St. WC2 | 6 West 57th St. | 896 Queen St. W.

Printed in the United States of America

To
my mother
Jennie Sharlin

ACKNOWLEDGEMENTS

I am grateful to the Sciences and Humanities Research Institute of Iowa State University for grants which made the completion of this book considerably easier.

I wish to thank Mrs. Carolyn Cameron for considerate help and careful typing of the manuscript.

I am indebted to the Iowa State University Library and the Princeton University Library for facilities where I could work, for essential material used in the book, and for exceptionally cooperative staff members.

Because of Tiby, my wife, this book was finished sooner and it is a better book.

Contents

THE CONVERGENT CENTURY

The Unification of Science in the Nineteenth Century

Introduction

This book takes as its major premise that the interpretation of the history of science must be done through the eyes of the past. The worst type of anachronism is the historian who intrudes himself into the past and judges which theory is correct, or almost correct, and who points out which theories are wrong from a modern point of view. Interpretation requires selection, and the selection must be based on what the past thought was important and what the historian recognizes as important to the history as a whole.

William Whewell, a nineteenth century historian and philosopher of science, wrote that what he sought in the history of science was the "common element and the common processes" found in scientific work. Then, he said, we shall have a philosophy of science. A history of science should, in effect, be describing the philosophy of science for the period considered. We want to find out what were the accepted methods and what were considered convincing results or what was a satisfactory explanation of the phenomena.

1

Through historical perspective we obtain a picture of the past by finding the lines that connect the main events and those lines that join the foreground of the picture (the present) with the background (the past).

Of the main lines of the history of nineteenth century science, the idea of convergence seemed paramount. Investigators discovered that energy was convertible into many different forms, such as heat, mechanical motion, electricity, and light. Many scientists believed that energy was going to supply the unifying concept, the great generalization, of the century. What did come from this view was the broadest theory of the century: the law of the conservation of energy.

Some saw the hope of convergence of theories as distant and unattainable. William Thomson believed that no property of matter would be explained until all properties were explained. "But though this consummation may never be reached by man," he said in the latter part of the century, "the progress of science may be, I believe will be, step by step towards it, on many different roads converging towards it from all sides."

Some nineteenth century scientists, like James Clerk Maxwell, saw the sciences as having a similarity of approach but not necessarily converging theories. Maxwell found these similarities suggestive in the formulation of theories by use of analogy. The method of analogy, especially as it was used with mechanical models, was a main line of nineteenth century science.

The British were most at home with the mechanical model. To the French, the model was a primitive and childlike attempt to understand nature. Yet the mechanical model, as used by such untutored and imaginative intellects as Dalton and Faraday, became the starting point of radically different approaches to some phenomena. Even such well educated British physicists and mathematicians as William Thomson and James Clerk Maxwell found models highly stimulating to the imagination. As a device for initiating theories the model was the most fruitful invention of the nineteenth century.

One aspect of the history that I tried to put into perspective was the relationship between mathematics and experiment in the making of theories. There appeared to be something which was tantalizingly close to a pattern in the alternation between mathematics and experiment. All that I was able to find was that within each field and during different times there were factors and personalities that produced a switch from one to the other method. I have tried to show in each case how the switch was brought about.

A universal in the whole history of science is controversy. In the nineteenth century, controversy was at the core of scientific investigation. Many of the major controversies were carried on across international boundaries. In the early part of the century the difference in outlook reflected the variety of backgrounds, both educational and institutional, of the scientists. The sometimes bitter dialogue resulted in modification and blending so that the resulting theory could not be credited to any one country. In the latter part of the century the adoption of the peculiarities of one country by others, the spread of the German university idea, for example, led to the moderation in the differences in point of view.

Each of the controversies helped to illustrate that theories were constructed, or invented, for the purpose of gaining an understanding of natural phenomena. Controversy shows better than anything else that theories are interpretations, not discoveries, of what is happening in the natural world. Maxwell said that it was a good thing to have two ways of looking at electrical phenomena and "to admit that there *are* two ways."

The history of science has appeared to me to be the story of men attempting to understand one aspect of the world through the observation of natural phenomena and the framing of theories. What follows is a history that shows how, in many ways, the nineteenth century was similar to all previous centuries and how the nineteenth century differed. The scientists of the nineteenth century made breaks with the past. They gave up the illusion of certainty and tried to develop new approaches to reality. An end was made to the use of imponderables which were the last vestige of ancient mysticism. A beginning was made in the more imaginative enterprise of making the imperceptible understandable without attempting to imagine final causes. No claim was made that these theories were *truth*. Those scientists of the last century were the first to have the courage to admit that they could never uncover the final cause of physical phenomena. We have accepted their belief that the object of the scientific pursuit of knowledge is not absolute truth but a continual striving for a better understanding of the actions involved in physical phenomena.

HAROLD I. SHARLIN

Ames, Iowa
August 1965

Electricity in Motion

1   Three articles that appeared in the *Philosophical Transactions of the Royal Society* in 1800 contained ideas that were to be the center of scientific activity during the first decades of the century. Coincidentally, the three ideas were the start of theories that were to become very closely related.

One article was Thomas Young's "Outlines of Experiments and Inquiries respecting Sound and Light." Young's analogy between sound and light were to lead him to the wave theory of light. The second article was a description of experiments conducted in an attempt to decompose muriatic acid. The author used electric pulses from a static electric machine to decompose the acid in preference to heat in order, he wrote, that "the phenomena that occur during the process, may be distinctly observed; and the comparison of the products . . . may be instituted with great exactness." Other chemists were to discover that electricity was a superb analytical tool and from this discovery develop the field of electrochemistry.

The third article to be published in that year 1800, and which was of such long range consequence, was in the form of a letter to the President of the Royal Society, Sir Joseph Banks. The letter was from a foreign member of the Society, Alessandro Volta. It was titled "On the Electricity excited by the mere Contact of Conducting Substances of different kinds." Volta described his invention, an "artificial electric organ," which was based on the fact that conductors, as well as the non-conductors used in static electric machines, were "exciters of electricity." His artificial electric organ was, Volta claimed, the same as the natural organ of the torpedo fish.[1]

The man who made this discovery, which was to have an immediate and widespread influence, was born in Como, Italy, in 1745. His father was a member of the impecunious, lesser nobility. Volta did not begin to speak until the age of four but then rapidly developed a facility with languages which included, besides his native Italian, Latin, French, English, Dutch, and Spanish. Shortly after his formal schooling was completed Volta began his experimental investigations into electricity. He was eighteen at the time. The results of his speculation were transmitted first to the French physicist Antoine Nollet in Paris and later to Giovanni Becaria, who was professor of physics at the University of Turin and the foremost Italian experimenter in electrostatics. Volta's international reputation was enlarged as a result of the researches reported in his correspondence, and he made several grand tours of Europe, during which he visited with scientists in such countries as Germany, France, Belgium, Russia, Switzerland, and Great Britain.

Volta's continuing interest in electricity was both speculative and inventive. In 1775 he invented an electrophorus which was an ingenious way of producing static electricity. In a letter communicated to the Royal Society in 1782, Volta described another invention, a highly sensitive indicating instrument for electricity. His scientific activity earned him a chair in physics at the University of Pavia in 1778. The Royal Society made him a Fellow in 1791 and awarded him one of its highest honors, the Copley Medal, in 1794. All of this research in electricity beginning in 1763 not only meant that Volta could speak with considerable authority on electrical matters but that this authority would be that of a man steeped in the study of static electricity.

Napoleon's conquest of Italy in 1801 was the occasion of the French discovery of Volta's work. Information of Volta's battery had been published in the *Philosophical Transactions,* but these were not being read in France because of the Napoleonic wars. Volta was invited to Paris by Napoleon, where he was feted and honored with titles and money. Napoleon, who fancied himself an amateur scientist, was particularly interested in electricity and he attended Volta's demonstrations before the French Academy. As a spur to further research Napoleon established prizes to be awarded to men making contributions to the study of electricity.

Ironically, the French Revolution, which benefited Volta so much, resulted in lasting damage to the career of another Italian scientist whose work provided the lead for Volta's battery. The unfortunate Italian was Luigi Galvani, who was professor of anatomy at the University of Bologna. Galvani refused to take an oath of allegiance to the republic established by the French in Italy and as a result he was stripped of all offices. An attempt was made to restore him to his former position in recognition of his scientific achievements, but the gesture came too late. His decline into poverty and melancholy ended with his death in 1798.

Galvani's approach to electricity was a distinct contrast with that of Volta. Galvani was a physiologist and was interested particularly in susceptibility of nerves to irritation. He also had some interest in electrical phenomena. In 1780 Galvani, "by chance," he said, noted a connection between his nerve experiments and electricity. The discharge of a static electric machine in his laboratory at the same time that a scalpel was touched to the crural nerve in a frog's leg produced violent convulsions in the leg. The chance happening intrigued Galvani, and he set about to "discover its hidden principle." After a series of experiments in which he tried to determine why the discharge of an electric machine, the presence of atmospheric electricity, and finally the mere contact of a metal loop to the frog's leg produced the same convulsions, he was led, he wrote, "to suspect that electricity is inherent in the animal itself." His suspicion was confirmed, he thought, by the observation that there was a circuit of "subtle nervous fluid," which was the cause of muscular action.[2] Galvani believed that all muscular action was a result of this discharge of electricity within the nervous system. The electricity here was the same as that collected in an ordinary

Leyden jar, but the important thing to him was that he had determined the cause of muscular activity: it was electricity. Galvani was not interested in determining the source of the electricity; apparently he believed it was "inherent" in the body. Galvani, as an anatomist, was interested in the physiological effects of the electricity: muscular motion.

The importance of his discovery, as he saw it, was that the animal organism contained electricity, and that his experiment with the metallic rods was a method of shorting this electricity and producing motion even when the animal was dead. Galvani's supporters decided that he had found a new form of electricity, which they labeled "Animal Electricity."

Volta, when he heard of Galvani's experiments, refused to accept the idea of a new electricity and that the body of the animal was the source. The body was, he insisted, the means of conducting the electricity that was actually produced by the metals. In 1799 Volta wrote: "The contact of different conductors . . . agitates or disturbs the electric fluid, or gives it a certain impulse."

Galvani's chance discovery was indeed remarkable, but what was its significance? If, as Galvani claimed, he had discovered a new electricity and that electricity was the cause of muscular action, then the whole thing was an object for physiologists to study. If the discovery was of a new source of electricity, the metal conductors, as Volta claimed, then the subject concerned physicists. The controversy was fanned by inter-university rivalry between Pavia and Bologna.

Volta does not seem to have been impressed with the theoretical significance of the discovery itself. When he wrote about the production of an electric impulse by dissimilar metals he cut off any possibility of further study. "Do not ask in what manner" the electric fluid was disturbed, Volta wrote a friend, "it is enough that it is a principle, and a general principle."[3] Volta bent his efforts in extending the general principle in order to increase the magnitude of the electric disturbance of two metals. He had no success. He was, in 1799, in the position of a chemist who is dealing with an unknown compound whose composition he thinks he knows but cannot be certain of because he does not have a large enough sample.

In 1800 Volta hit upon the method of magnifying the power that Galvani had discovered. Volta alternated layers of two different metals which he separated by brine-soaked cardboard. At last Volta had a large enough sample to prove that conductors when properly arranged produced electricity. The result far exceeded the immediate purpose of proving Galvani's supporters wrong. What really astounded Volta was that this new source, the battery, far surpassed the effects of a Leyden jar, which produced only a single pulse of electricity. These were the findings that Volta reported in his letter to the Royal Society.

The apparatus that Volta thought would "no doubt, astonish you" resembled the Leyden jar in the effects it produced except that Volta had made something that had "an inexhaustible charge, a perpetual action or impulse on the electric fluid. . . ."[4] "This endless circulation of the electric fluid (*this perpetual motion*) may appear paradoxical and even inexplicable," Volta conceded, "but it is no less true and real; and you feel it, as I may say, with your hands."[5] This last was a reference to the physiological methods scientists used in detecting the electricity; one of these methods was shock.

In one place in the letter Volta referred to "my *electromotive* apparatus" and added parenthetically that "we must give new names to instruments that are new not only in their form, but in . . . the principle on which they depend."[6]

The importance of Volta's invention to chemical analysis was grasped immediately. His letter to Sir Joseph Banks announcing the battery was shown to two men, Dr. William Nicholson and Sir Anthony Carlisle, who immediately began a series of experiments with the battery. Their findings were published just months later in July, 1800. Nicholson applauded Volta's research into "the nature and laws of electricity" which, he wrote, "must for ever remove the doubt whether galvanism be an electrical phenomenon." The decomposing effects of static electricity had been investigated and the findings, for instance, those on muriatic acid mentioned above, had been reported in the *Philosophical Transactions*. Nicholson and Carlisle, the chemists, were surprised that Volta, the physicist, did not "observe the chemical phenomena of galvanism."

The two experimenters had used a drop of water to make

better electrical contact with their battery. It was Carlisle who noted the "disengagement of gas around the touching wire." They had discovered the way of decomposing water by means of Volta's battery. In Nicholson's words, this discovery "gave birth to a variety of speculations and projects of experiments."[7]

The rate at which experimental results were announced by a number of widely dispersed scientists was a measure of the enthusiasm engendered by the new analytical tool, which was at the same time a new mystery. Rapid progress was attributable to the increasing rate of diffusion of information, which was promoted by journals such as *Nicholson's Journal of Natural Philosophy, Chemistry and the Arts, The Philosophical Magazine, The Philosophical Transactions of the Royal Society, Gilbert's Annalen,* and *Annales de Chimie,* to name a few.

Humphry Davy, who had just been appointed professor of chemistry at the Royal Institution, took an active interest in the new discoveries.

The Royal Institution, in the opinion of its founder, Count Rumford, was primarily for giving alms and useful employment to the poor in addition to introducing new inventions and improvements for their benefit. At its formation in 1799, the Institution was described as a "public Institution for diffusing the knowledge and facilitating the general introduction of useful mechanical inventions and improvements, and for teaching by courses of philosophical lectures and experiments the application of science to the common purposes of life."[8] The Institution was from the beginning started in a much different direction, dictated by the personality and ambitions of Humphry Davy. It was he who interpreted the charter to mean original research and public lectures to the middle and upper classes. The result was that the Royal Institution contributed not at all to the amelioration of the poor; but the Institution can claim credit for the support of research of Davy and Faraday, whose work contributed greatly to the shaping of early nineteenth century science.

Davy's work on the voltaic pile followed the Nicholson-Carlisle lead in that it was primarily electrochemical. In the fall of 1800, Davy began to publish the results of his work. He was not only interested in what the battery could do in chemical analysis but was intrigued by the question of an explanation of how the battery worked. There were not enough facts, he believed, "to explain the exact mode of operation," but it was reasonable to conclude that "the chemical changes connected with" the battery were "*somehow* the cause of the electrical effects it produces."[9] There was, it seemed, a chemical cause to the voltaic piles as well as a chemical effect.

The work of Davy and other experimenters amassed information that appeared to Jöns Jacob Berzelius to demonstrate an electro-chemical theory of chemical combination. This theory came from joining the idea of electrical attraction with chemical affinity in what was called the dualistic theory of chemical combination. This facet of the theory of the electric force is treated in another chapter. What is of concern here is the physical effects of the electric force.

The attractive effects of a charge of electricity that had been accumulated on a piece of amber had been noted in Grecian times. The similarity between electric attraction and magnetic attraction was noted at least as early as the Middle Ages. Some investigators were struck by the similarities and analogies between the two forces, but there were too many differences for anyone to seriously claim that electricity and magnetism were identical.

The study of magnetism followed a course separate from electricity during the eighteenth and early nineteenth century. The magnetism of the earth was of practical and international interest because of its importance to navigation. Interest was renewed in this topic with the publcation of *Magnetismus der Erde* by a Norwegian in 1819. The Norwegian parliament was so impressed by the book that it voted funds for a magnetic expedition to be conducted along the north of Europe and Asia in 1828-30. The parliament in that same session refused to vote funds so that the king could build a castle at Christiana, thereby indicating, one can conclude, the direction in which political forces were moving in the nineteenth century: less money for monarchy, more funds for the general good—including science.

In 1825 magnetic observations at Paris and at Kasan, Russia, were compared, and the marked variance in the readings was termed "magnetic storms" by Alexander von Humboldt. The stations were 47 degrees longitude apart. Humboldt prevailed upon the Russian government to establish magnetic observatories in a chain across the whole empire, extending as far east as Alaska.

Carl F. Gauss, who was professor of mathematics at Göttingen, developed improved instruments and techniques for taking magnetic observations. He organized eighteen stations from Dublin to Petersburg where readings were taken beginning in 1835. The observations consisted of a series conducted six times a year for a period of 24 hours in intervals of 5 minutes. Gauss and Wilhelm Weber began publishing the *Results of the Magnetic Association* in 1836. The British Association for the Advancement of Science adopted the idea of promoting magnetic observatories as a project befitting their mission. The idea spread. The Rajah of Travancore established an observatory in India. The Pasha of Egypt founded one in Cairo. In Austria, Spain, Bavaria, and the United States, magnetic observatories were founded where simultaneous readings were taken using the same type instruments and the same methods. The only international scientific enterprise that could compare was the astronomical observatories that had a longer history. But no better evidence is needed for the growing international aspects of nineteenth century science than the worldwide network of magnetic observatories.

This was the age of the clipper ship to be followed shortly by the steamship era, which so shortened the time of intercontinental travel as to make the world into one economic unit. The network of magnetic stations made their contribution to this advance. Whewell described the observatories: "Such a scheme, combining world-wide extent with the singleness of action of an individual mind, is hitherto without parallel."[10]

The British Association *Report* of 1845 extolled "a growing recognition of the importance, both for science and for practical life, of forming exact observers of nature." The *Report* noted there were only a few opportunities for training observers and they were in astronomy only. "Experience has shown," Wilhelm Weber wrote the Association, "that magnetic observations may serve as excellent training schools in this respect."[11]

It may seem surprising that with all of this concentrated effort magnetic theory was not advanced appreciably by all of the accumulated data. In the case of terrestrial temperature readings, as we shall see in the next chapter, Fourier was able to formulate some ideas on the transmission of heat from a wealth of data similar to the magnetic readings. The difference was that the temperature information was applicable to a relatively concentrated area of the earth, whereas one would have to consider the whole globe at once to use the magnetic readings for theory building. Terrestial magnetism was too extensive a topic for clear comprehension.

The history of the study of magnetism illustrates that there is more to formulating theories than just collecting enough data. Theories were devised by finding a connection with established concepts, by establishing a relationship, or by indicating an analogy. In the case of magnetism, ideas were built on the relationship with electricity. A likely place to begin would be with the question: what of the similarity between the attractive power of magnetism and electricity?

In the summer of 1820, Hans Christian Oersted, professor of physics at the University of Copenhagen, announced that he had established a connection between magnetic and electric force. Oersted had been vainly trying to establish this relationship for over five years. He had found that the "electric conflict" that was produced when an electric current passed through a wire "can only act upon magnetic particles of matter. All non-magnetic bodies seem to be penetrable through electric conflict; but magnetic bodies . . . seem to resist the passage of this conflict, whence it is that they can be moved by the impulse of contending forces."

An electric charge, it was known, repelled or attracted another charge just as like magnetic poles repelled and unlike poles attracted. Now for the first time Oersted had produced a force between electricity and magnetism. What he had found was that a magnetic compass needle was affected when a wire carrying current was brought near. First he had found that only an electric current would produce the "electric conflict" and as expected the force was "dispersed in the surrounding space" around the conductor. The totally unexpected part of his discovery was that the magnetic needle was not attracted towards the current-carrying wire nor repelled from it. The needle assumed a position at right angles to the wire. Oersted concluded that the "conflict performs gyrations" around the conductor.[12]

Oersted's discovery was described at a meeting of the French Academy in September, 1820. The speaker was François Arago, who had just returned from a scientific excursion abroad. The Academy's interest in electricity had not waned since Volta had visited there at Napoleon's invitation. Several French scientists began at once to duplicate Oersted's experiment and to plan additional ones.

One week after Arago's announcement, a member of the Academy, André-Marie Ampère, reported that there was also a force exerted between two parallel wires carrying current. This result was fast in coming, but Ampère was to demonstrate by intensive work over the next few years that his work was of an original character and that he could sustain the originality.

André-Marie Ampère was born in Lyons in 1775. His father had retired from being a merchant, and it was he who became his son's first and almost only teacher. The Revolution left no French scientist's life untouched, but its impact on Ampère was particularly tragic. His father was executed in 1793, and as a result Ampère was mentally incapacitated for a year. When he came to himself, Ampère began to give private lessons in mathematics. His brilliance and ambition had not been dimmed. A paper, which he published in 1802 on the mathematical theory of probability as applied to games of chance, brought him to the attention of the leading French mathematicians. Ampère was appointed professor of analysis at *Ecole Polytechnique* in 1809 and became a member of the French Academy in 1814. By 1820 Ampère was well established, but as an original mathematical theorist, supposedly, he was beyond his prime. He was forty-five years old. But Ampère's work in electromagnetic theory was his best work, and it placed him in the front rank of scientists in that or any other field.

Beginning in that fall of 1820 Ampère published a series of papers that reported the results of his experimental and mathematical work, all of which were reviewed and summarized in 1826 in his *Mémoire sur la théorie des phénomènes électrodynamiques uniquement déduite de l'expérience*. That Ampère was conscious that he was dealing with a phenomena distinct from the effects of static electricity is apparent from his invention of a suitable vocabulary. He coined the word *electrodynamic* to designate the "true character" of the phenomena that were produced by "electricity in motion." *Electrostatics* was to be used for all those phenomena of attraction and repulsions produced by "electricity at rest."

Two sorts of effects were produced by electricity. The first was that produced by an electric charge on an insulator and was called *electric tension* by Ampère. The second was produced by, he said, "electric current." These effects were only manifest as long as the voltaic circuit was complete as shown by Oersted's experiment and the electrical decomposition of compounds. Break the circuit and the magnetic needle returned to a position of rest and the chemical action ceased. Ampère reported the results of some new experiments with current electricity. He found that two parallel wires carrying current in the same direction were attracted to each other and repelled when the currents moved in opposite directions.

Notice, he wrote, that attraction and repulsion of electric currents were in opposite sense from the effects of static electricity, "electric tension." The peculiar force produced by current electricity ceased when the circuit was broken, but then the force of electric tension would attract light bodies. In addition, he found that the attraction between electric currents did not stop when the two conductors touched; whereas in the case of static electricity, once an object touched a charged body it was afterwards repelled.

Ampère placed two conductors so that one pivoted freely with respect to the other. He found that the moveable conductor turned until it became parallel to the fixed conductor and in such a way that the currents were in the same direction. "From which it follows," he concluded, "that in the mutual action of two electric currents the directive action and the attractive or repulsive action depend on the same principle and are only different effects of one and the same action." What accounts for the action between an electric current and a magnet and between two magnets? A magnet must consist, Ampère believed, of particles with electric currents circulating around them; so that all forces produced by electrodynamic action, whether it be between two currents or a magnet and a current or two magnets, were the results of "electricity in motion." "It is thus that we come to this unexpected result," Ampère said, "that the phenomena of the magnet are produced by electricity and that there is no other difference between the two poles of a magnet than their positions with respect to the currents of which the magnet is composed."

Ampère claimed that the generality of his idea of circulating currents was proof enough of its correctness. He claimed for his theory the ability to reduce "to a single principle three sorts of actions which the totality of the phenomena proves to result from a common cause and which cannot be reduced to one principle in any other way."[13] The idea of circulating currents as the source of electrodynamic forces was a fruitful physical concept. It did offer a satisfactory explanation for the forces between currents on conductors, between magnets and current carrying conductors, and between magnets themselves. The idea of circulating currents also appeared to be a reasonable explanation for the fact that these forces were of a continuing nature.

Ampère's most important contribution to electrodynamic theory was the development of mathematical equations whereby these forces could be calculated for all conditions. Ampère belonged to the school of thinking that viewed physical phenomena as the result of forces exerted between particles. All that was necessary was two particles; no third thing was required. This outlook had an ancient heritage, at least as old as Democritus, and has variously been attributed through history to a group who saw all nature as composed of particles and the void. In the nineteenth century the idea was known as "action-at-a-distance."

Ampère at first found that he could not solve his electrodynamic equations. The equations were, in this condition, no better than mathematical postulates. They were an interesting representation of a physical theory, but unless they could be solved they were without much significance. At this point he employed his idea of circulating currents in order to solve the equations. He not only was able to solve his equations but the solution checked with previous experimental results and was a basis for further experimentation. "Action-at-a-distance" therefore became a forceful theory with which to contend. Other scientists, like Michael Faraday, who could not conceive of a force being transmitted without an intervening medium had the burden of proof placed on them.

Ampère's work bears all of the characteristics of the French school of mathematicians who turned their attention to physical problems. They, like the experimental scientists, had to make physical suppositions, but unlike the experimentalists, they were not tied down by attempts to picture reality. The reason for the greater generality of the mathematician's work is that he ventures only to show the numerical relationship in nature. You might say that the mathematician does not attempt to understand the forces of nature; he devises ways of using these forces. Ampère's equations can be and are used for designing electrical machinery. Yet they cannot, and do not profess to, portray the forces of nature in a way that can be comprehended by the intellect of man.

Heat... Imponderable or Imperceptible

2   The two phenomena, heat and electricity, appeared to the nineteenth century scientist to have a remarkable resemblance. They were both imperceptible; that is, they could only be studied by means of secondary effects. There was no way of dealing with them directly; no one could see heat or electricity, and the senses gave no indication of their existence unless burned or shocked.

It was this difficulty in perceiving them that raised the question of their true nature. Were they imponderable substances, which in the case of heat was called caloric and in the case of electricity, the electric fluid? Or were heat and electricity really effects produced by imperceivable forces?

This discovery of their convertibility provided another way of studying heat. Use of analogy between the two, as we shall see in a later chapter, lent considerable aid to the difficult task of conceptualizing electricity.

Two theories of heat were current at the beginning of the nineteenth century: the older theory, which considered heat as an imponderable substance, persisted along with the new Rumford-Davy theory. Count Rumford's experiments at the end of the eighteenth century raised serious doubts about the materiality of heat. He had applied a blunted cutting tool to a casting of a cannon and found that there apparently was no limit to the amount of heat that was generated by this friction. If the cannon contained a substance, caloric, assuredly the supply was limited. Perhaps the supply was limited, some argued, but Rumford had not exhausted the supply contained within the cannon. The caloric theory had been strained in order to explain the Rumford cannon experiments, and many believed that a telling blow had been delivered to the theory. Humphry Davy advocated a new theory in which "the immediate cause of the phenomena of heat is motion, and the laws of its communication are precisely the same as the laws of the communication of motion."[1] If one took this view, the key to the study of heat was mechanics or the laws of motion. But how was one to apply these laws to countless particles that moved in a random fashion?

Rumford was not sure what heat was, but he was sure that it was not a material substance. Rumford's skepticism was sensible. He wrote that "even though the mechanism of heat should, in fact, turn out to be one of those mysteries of nature that are beyond the reach of human intelligence, this ought by no means to discourage us, or even lessen our ardor, in our attempts to investigate the laws of its operations."[2]

Two notable contributions were made to heat theory in the early nineteenth century. They were Jean Baptiste Joseph Fourier's memoir of 1807 and Nicolas Leonard Sadi Carnot's paper published in 1824. Carnot's hypothesis described the conditions for the most efficient means of using heat for producing mechanical power. His use of the idea of a perfect engine remains valid in spite of the fact that he based his work on the caloric theory. Fourier's memoir, a mathematically elegant description of the rate of conduction of heat, used mathematical deduction, which was new to the study of heat. Fourier's approach was to be a model for all those who were to use mathematics in their analysis of heat and electricity.

Joseph Fourier was born in 1768. He began his studies at a Benedictine military school, where he first became interested in mathematics. He was later refused admission to an artillery school because he was "not noble." Instead he entered an abbey with the intention of becoming a Benedictine monk. The French Revolution intervened.

When Napoleon went to Egypt in 1798 on what was primarily a campaign to cut the British off from India, he took along a group of France's leading scientists. His intent was to recapture the glory of the ancient world. Napoleon relied upon Fourier to help transform the scientific retinue into the Institute of Egypt. Fourier served as permanent secretary to the Institute. While in Egypt, he was also sent by Napoleon on some difficult diplomatic missions.

Fourier was not a scientist dependent on government aid. He was a scientist whose vocation became government administration. On his return to France, Fourier was made a prefect of a department and he took up residence at Grenoble. While fulfilling these duties he had time to compose his *Analytical Theory of Heat*. The idea of this theory was first published as papers and it was finally released as a book in 1822. After Napoleon's fall, Fourier was removed as prefect. It was his association with the revolutionary regime that delayed his admission into the *Académie des Sciences* until 1817.

Fourier's contributions to science were of broad generality and were highly theoretical in nature; that is, his work was the type that is not associated with practical applications. Fourier stated that he was attracted to the study of heat because of "the rigorous exactness of its elements and the analytical difficulties peculiar to it." Yet he seemed to feel that his study had to be justified. Fourier maintained that the study of heat would always attract mathematicians because of the challenge of its theory, "and above all by the extent and usefulness of its applications" to "the operations of the arts, domestic uses and civil economy."[3]

PRELIMINARY DISCOURSE

Primary causes are unknown to us; but are subject to simple and constant laws, which may be discovered by observation, the study of them being the object of natural philosophy.[4]

That was the way Fourier began his book, *The Analytical*

Theory of Heat. By primary causes he meant the nature of heat. He was not ducking the controversy as to whether heat was an imponderable substance or the effect of molecular motion. These were "uncertain hypotheses" and furthermore they were not necessary to discover the "constant laws" of heat which could only be found with "the aid of mathematical analysis."[5]

Mechanics was a study that Fourier considered ideal in every way and he meant to place the study of heat on a par with it. For one thing: "Heat, like gravity, penetrates every substance of the universe," and he was confident that the theory of heat "will hereafter form one of the most important branches of general physics." In addition, the history of mechanics from Archimedes to Newton, Fourier claimed, had shown that "the most diverse phenomena are subject to a small number of fundamental laws." Mechanics was an ideal for which the science of heat should strive, but the laws of mechanics themselves were of no use to the study of heat for, he said, "whatever may be the range of mechanical theories, they do not apply to the effects of heat. These make a special order of phenomena. . . ."

Fourier's approach was to first "distinguish and define with precision the elementary properties which determine the action of heat." His way of distinguishing or selecting the elementary properties was to determine in what ways bodies differed from each other in their reaction to heat. Fourier thought that he had found three of these properties which could serve as the basis for analysis of heat. The first property was the body's power to *contain* heat, second, *to receive or transmit* heat across its surfaces, and third, to *conduct* heat through the interior of its mass. "These are the three specific qualities," Fourier wrote, "which our theory clearly distinguishes and shews how to measure."[6]

The French Academy of Science proposed as its prize question for 1812: "To give the mathematical theory of the propagation of heat, and to compare this theory with exact observations." The prize was awarded to Fourier, as all expected, because he was the only one up to that time who was using the mathematical approach to the study of heat. As early as 1807 he had read a paper before the Academy on heat; the paper was the first presentation by Fourier, or anyone else, of a method of dealing with heat mathematically. Fourier's complete exposition of his theory was made in *Théorie Analytique de la Chaleur*, which was published in 1822.

The book dealt with a variety of questions on heat from one as general as the chapter "The Equation of the movement of Heat" to the solution of such specific problems as finding the general expression "Of the Linear and Varied Movement of Heat in a Ring."

The statement of the problem to be solved, for the scientist, is the way he fashions his probe. It must penetrate below the superficial but not thrust beyond the answerable. Fourier stated the problem of propagation of heat as being a question of determining the temperature of a given body at any instant. For this condition to have generality the temperature of the whole body must be changing. Supposing, Fourier said, that a uniformly heated body were moved to a cooler place. Heat would immediately begin to leave from the surfaces and, if it be imagined that the body itself is divided into an infinity of layers, a quantity of heat will be transferred at each instant from one layer to the adjacent one. Fourier asked the reader to imagine that each molecule of the body had a thermometer that indicated its temperature at every instant. The object of the mathematical analysis was to find a general solution for this situation. "It is required to express the successive states by analytical formulae," he wrote, "so that we may know at any given instant the temperatures indicated by each thermometer, and compare the quantities of heat which flow during the same instant, between two adjacent layers, or into the surrounding medium."[7]

The way Fourier approached the problem of the transmission of heat became a guide for other nineteenth century scientists who were confronted with problems of similar intricacy. James Clerk Maxwell, who later undertook to do for the study of electricity what Fourier had accomplished in the study of heat, admired the way in which Fourier had avoided "the intricacies arising from the arbitrary conditions of the problem" by employing "powerful analytical methods . . . to express the varied conditions. . . ." So remarkably general were Fourier's methods, Maxwell said, that "in every branch of physics, when the investigation turns upon the expression of arbitrary conditions, we have to follow the method which Fourier first pointed out in his 'Theory of Heat.' "[8]

The problem that intrigued Fourier most was that of the variation of terrestrial temperatures which, he said, "presents one of the most beautiful applications of the theory of heat." Temperatures taken of the soil over long periods of time indicated that at some depths there were no annual or daily variations of temperature. This steady temperature had different values depending on the latitude, that is, distance, from the equator. What made this such an interesting question for someone interested in the propagation of heat was the steadiness of the temperatures below the surface in spite of the variations of heat transmitted to the surface. These variations were caused by the change in solar heat received by the earth from sunup to sundown each day and by a greater change in heat due to the seasons.

The problem in Fourier's hands becomes one of a spherical body (the earth) in which every internal molecule has a fixed temperature determined by its position. "The problem is reducible to the hypothesis that every point of a vast sphere is affected by periodic temperatures," Fourier said. "Analysis then tells us according to what law . . . the fixed value of the underground temperature is deduced from the variable temperatures observed at the surface." The data available for testing Fourier's theory of heat as applied to terrestrial temperatures was worldwide and was available for long periods of time. Not only was this application an important verification of his theory but the mathematics he developed for dealing with periodic variations was one of the most widely used types of analysis in the nineteenth century. Fourier analysis became commonplace for work in mechanics, electricity, light, and sound.

The results of Fourier's work were expressed in the calculus of partial differential equations which could not be solved. This outcome would seem to have been a refutation of his method because, as Fourier said, as long as there were no numerical answers, "the solutions may be said to remain incomplete and useless, and the truth which it is proposed to discover is no less hidden in the formulae of analysis than it was in the physical problem itself." But the way a mathematician sees equations, they represent relations between physical quantities. The way out of Fourier's dilemma was to find another way of calculating the indeterminate quantities. He had to break the complicated, insoluble expression into its simpler soluble parts. The quantities, he said, on which heat transmission was dependent were (1) containing, (2) transmitting, and (3) conducting of heat. These could not be determined directly, so he expressed them in terms of length, time, weight, temperature, and quantity of heat. The technique is similar to finding distance by multiplying velocity and time. "We have applied ourselves with much care to this purpose," he announced, "and we have been able to overcome the difficulty in all the problems of which we have treated. . . ."⁹

Herein lies the key to the generality of Fourier's mathematical equations. Not only were they applicable to all problems regarding the transmission of heat, whether it be in an iron ring or in the earth itself, but the method was applicable to other areas of physics. For example, the transmission of energy in the form of electricity, light, or sound has been found to be analogous to the movement of heat. In each of these cases three primary factors analogous to containing, transmitting, and conducting of heat are calculated by putting these factors in terms of physical quantities analogous to Fourier's five quantities: length, time, temperature, weight, and quantity of heat. For electricity, for example, the quantities would be length, time, voltage, weight, and quantity of electricity in coulombs.

Fourier's partial differential equations and his method of solving them never ceased to amaze mathematicians and physicists of the nineteenth century. Their generality extends to the expression of the motion of a violin string as well as the motion of a compressed spring. Fourier would have been pleased with Michael Pupin's use of his equations to solve a problem in long distance telephone transmission, because Fourier always believed the scientist should be interested in application to "domestic uses and civil economy."

Fourier's success helped to clarify and extend the using of mathematics in scientific investigation. The relationship between mathematics and the study of nature was reciprocal, according to Fourier. "Profound study of nature is the most fertile source of mathematical discoveries," he wrote. This study helps to focus investigation on the important questions, thereby eliminating those that are vague and "without issue." The study of nature, he thought, was also a "sure method of forming analysis itself" because the scientist thereby attends to "fundamental elements" which appear in all natural effects. One mathematical equation that had previously been considered only by geometers had been found applicable to as widely different things as motion of light in the atmosphere, the diffusion of heat in a solid, and was useful in the chief problems of probability.

Nature is a source for and a guide to mathematical analysis, and in turn mathematics serves in the study of nature. Mathematics, Fourier said, "brings together phenomena the most diverse, and discovers the hidden analogies which unite them." Besides awakening man's imagination, mathematics extends his senses beyond his mortal limitations. Fourier wrote:

> If matter escapes us, as that of air and light, by its extreme tenuity, if bodies are placed far from us in the immensity of space, if man wishes to know the aspect of the heavens at successive epochs separated by a great number of centuries, if the actions of gravity and of heat are exerted in the interior of the earth at depths which will be always inaccessible, mathematical analysis can yet lay hold of the laws of these phenomena. It makes them present and measurable, and seems to be a faculty of the human mind destined to supplement the shortness of life and the imperfection of the senses. . . .[10]

And finally, mathematics can be used to guide future experiments. Fourier was certain that his new theory on the conduction of heat would foster further investigations all over the earth under various conditions. Observations would need to be taken on the mountains, in the lakes, and in the different forms of matter, that is, solids, liquids, and gases. The next step in the study of heat, he thought, was experiment, "for mathematical analysis can deduce from general and simple phenomena the expression of the laws of nature; but special application of these laws to very complex effects demands a long series of exact observations."[11]

The importance of Fourier's work on heat to scientific theory was no greater than his influence in the use of mathematics for scientific investigation. For Fourier, mathematics was not merely a convenient way of expressing the results of experiments, it was a way of *doing* science. He had taken propositions about the transmission of heat and, instead of testing them experimentally, he had deduced the consequences of his ideas, mathematically. In his view of mathematics, Fourier was opposed by experimentalists like Michael Faraday who knew very little mathematics. Such people found the expression of results in mathematical terms difficult to understand and they sought to have the mathematics "translated." To the experimentalist who understood little of mathematics, representation of nature in this way was unnecessarily obscure.

"It might be asked, why in physical science generalization so readily takes the mathematical form," Henri Poincaré, the French mathematician, said at the end of the century. The role of mathematics in scientific investigation was still being discussed, but by the philosophers of science who, like Poincaré, were evaluating the work of scientists like Fourier. The experience of the century affirmed what Fourier had said at the beginning. "Mathematics teaches us," Poincaré wrote, "in fact, to combine like with like." Fourier had said that mathematical analysis could lay hold of the laws of inaccessible phenomena. Poincaré echoed this view when he said that the object of mathematics "is to divine the result of a combination without having to reconstruct that combination element by element."[12]

By 1835 mathematical analysis of heat based on Fourier's approach appeared to have reached a limit of usefulness. A report to the British Association for the Advancement of Science complained that "the direction which the speculations of our mathematicians concerning heat have thus taken, has not been in all respects favourable to the progress of the subject as a branch of experimental and inductive science." According to the report, the "great beauty and curiosity" of the mathematics had

led many into "that deep and charmed labyrinth much longer
and further than the demands of physical science required. . . ."

William Whewell, who wrote the report for the British
Association, was an accomplished mathematician, so that his
complaint that the mathematical treatment of heat could have
been of a "simpler kind" was not prompted by any difficulty he
had with the subject. He thought that simpler mathematics
would have "brought a far wider circle of intellect to bear upon
the inquiry; and thus would have tended much to the diffusion
of sound knowledge, and, not improbably, to the promotion of
further discovery."[13]

The way out of the labyrinth, according to some, was experiment. James Prescott Joule's experiments uncovered facts about
the nature of heat that no mathematical analysis could have
found.

James Prescott Joule was the last of the wealthy amateur
scientists to do original and important work. He and people like
him were eliminated from future advance in science, and it was
not because they did not have the investment necessary for high-
powered experimental equipment of the new science. The Joules
and the Faradays became rare because they did not have the
intellectual investment needed to work in the advancing science.
By the middle of the nineteenth century any young man wishing
to take up science would find it essential to have a university
training in mathematics. It was not for want of equipment but
the lack of formal training in mathematics (this was one field
where it was virtually impossible to be self-taught) that blocked
amateurs from science in that period.

Joule was born in Manchester in 1818. He was the son of a
wealthy brewery owner. The many aspects of brewery operation,
mechanical and chemical, first raised technical and scientific
questions for Joule, and the business provided funds for his
private scientific investigations. Since he was not required in the
operation of the brewery, he also had the leisure for his work.

After Joule finished his ordinary school education, he and his
brother were sent by their father to study with John Dalton.
Dalton was still taking private students to earn a living. The
brothers were eager to learn chemistry from the originator of

the atomic theory, but Dalton filled their daily lessons with drill in ordinary arithmetic. He would not begin the study of chemistry with the boys until they had mastered trigonometry and logarithmic tables. This was difficult work for boys but hardly to be considered advanced mathematics even in that day. The mathematics provided the boys with enough background for an introduction to chemistry and, meagre as it was, it was still enough to enable James Joule to teach himself the fundamentals of electricity. Dalton's insistence on a foundation in mathematics before beginning the study of chemistry imbued Joule with the quantitative approach which he was to follow throughout his career.

Joule's superiority as an experimentalist was evident in his carefully and accurately designed apparatus. It was this accuracy and his confidence in it that enabled him to draw conclusions, as some critics pointed out, based on only hundredths of a degree of temperature.

Joule's dedication to scientific research is illustrated by a story which William Thomson told. Thomson met Joule one day in the country and Joule was carrying what appeared at first to be a walking stick but turned out to be a specially designed, long thermometer. Joule would not trust the instrument in the carriage that was traveling slowly behind him. In the carriage was Joule's bride of a few days. He had decided to take advantage of his honeymoon travels to collect data on the heat of waterfalls. We are told that his bride did not mind.

Science was a career for Joule. He was not merely a wealthy man filling up his leisure hours dabbling in science. At one time he allowed himself to become a candidate for the chair of natural philosophy at St. Andrew's. One friend believed that Joule would have been successful, but one of the electors of St. Andrew's thought that Joule's slight physical deformity ruled against him. The last work that Joule carried out was recalculating the mechanical equivalent of heat. By that time, around 1875, he did not have enough to pay for the cost of the experiments. A dilettante would not have continued. Joule finished the experiments with a grant supplied by the Royal Society. This last paper was published in the *Philosophical Transactions of the Royal Society* in 1878.

Joule's experimental work began with attempts to improve the efficiency of electric motors. In one of his first published papers he indicated that his interest was practical application and not theoretical knowledge. "I can hardly doubt," he wrote in 1839, "that electro-magnetism will ultimately be substituted for steam to propel machinery." He even hoped that the cost of operating an electric motor could be "reduced *ad infinitum*," but he cautiously added, "It is, however, yet to be determined how far the effects of magnetic electricity may disappoint these expectations."[14]

Standards of measurement were needed in order to compare the efficiency of the motors. Joule's first step was to establish a uniform means of measuring electric currents for, as he said, "the great difficulty, if not impossibility, of understanding experiments and comparing them with one another, arises in general from incomplete descriptions of apparatus and from the arbitrary and vague numbers which are used to characterize electric currents." Electric science had advanced to the stage where "greater precision" was "imperatively demanded."[15]

Each of Joule's succeeding papers shows how he changed from an amateur tinkering with motors to an experimental scientist eager to try new ideas. To learn about the subjects of electricity and heat, he read the journals. He was thereby introduced to these sciences, not through the accepted tradition which he would have gotten from a formal education, but through reading about new and provisional ideas in the journals. His first papers were of the kind in which amateurs report how they have by mechanical cunning been able to improve apparatus. These were published in Sturgeon's *Annals of Electricity*.

Then in 1841 Joule's papers began to be published in the *Philosophical Magazine* and they give evidence of a broadened outlook. His footnotes show that he had been reading *Annales de Chimie, Philosophical Transactions of the Royal Society,* and Faraday's *Experimental Researches.* About this time also his papers were being read before the Literary and Philosophical Society of Manchester before they were published in the *Philosophical Magazine.*

He remarked at the opening of a paper published in 1841 in the *Philosophical Magazine*: "There are few facts in science more interesting than those which establish a connexion between heat and electricity."[16] The article was titled, "On the Heat Evolved by Metallic Conductors of Electricity, and in the Cells of a Battery during Electrolysis." Joule found that the connection between heat and electricity furnished a means for measuring electricity. The quantity of electricity was proportional to the heat it produced. In this paper he announced that he had established the fact that *the heat which is generated in a given time . . . is proportional to the resistance to conduction . . . multiplied by the square of the intensity of the current.* This statement has since become known as Joule's law.

"On the Calorific Effects of Magneto-Electricity, and on the Mechanical Equivalent of Heat" was read by Joule at the British Association for the Advancement of Science meeting in Cork in 1843. The first part of the paper dealt with an experimentalist's problem. If heat was a state of vibration and not a substance, then when a generator was used in experiments, was it not possible that the motion of the generator coil produced heat as well as electricity? He then reported the results of a series of tests the first of which was conducted on April 15 and the fifteenth on June 19. Joule declared that the generator coils produced electricity only. Having satisfied himself that the heat produced in his experiments was the result of the electricity only, he asked himself "whether a constant ratio existed between" heat and "the mechanical power" that produced it.

To determine the ratio he decided that he had only to repeat the first group of experiments and to construct some means of measuring the power used in turning the generator. Here he exhibited his skill as an experimenter who could devise apparatus that would be simple, and thereby free from error, and at the same time that would give results that could be used to answer a specific question. Joule used weights tied to the axle of the generator. The amount of the weights and their fall through a measured distance were used to calculate the mechanical equivalent supplied to the generator which produced an electric current which, in turn, was converted to heat.

The experiments that determined the equivalent of mechanical energy required to produce a unit of heat energy were as free from error as a careful worker like Joule could make them. He even estimated the amount of heat dissipated by sparking. The calculated value of 838 foot-pounds as the mechanical equivalent of heat necessary to raise the temperature of a pound of water one degree was remarkably good for the first attempt.

In the conclusion of his paper Joule returned to the original objective of determining the practicability of electric motors for industrial use. After calculating the number of foot-pounds that could be obtained when a zinc battery was used to drive a motor, Joule concluded that "it is evident that the electromagnetic engine, worked by the voltaic batteries at present used, will never supersede steam in an economical point of view."

No one has since found a way of economically powering electric motors by batteries. On the other hand, the economy of driving electric motors with electricity obtained from generators driven by steam turbines or water turbines has been well established. All forms of energy, including atomic power, are more economically applied by converting them to electricity. Joule's experiments that demonstrated convertibility were part of the outlook that formed the theoretical basis for the nineteenth century's new age of power.

Joule drew other conclusions, besides the negative one on use of electric motors, from his experiments. Although these other ideas seem to be added parenthetically and in postscripts, they do show where his research had led him. Others were gradually to change their views on heat as a result of reading Joule. One conclusion set down in the postscript was that heat was not a substance. "We shall be obliged to admit that Count Rumford was right," he wrote, "in attributing the heat evolved by boring cannon to friction, and not . . . to any change in the capacity of the metal."

He had arrived at another belief, also inserted in the postscript. He was "satisfied that the grand agents of nature are, by the Creator's fiat, *indestructible;* and that wherever mechanical force is expended, an exact equivalent of heat is *always* obtained."[17] It was only by firmly holding to this belief, and it was only a belief since he had not proved it by any means, that Joule could continue his experiments of the mechanical equivalent of heat. He had to assume that when one type of force was converted to another, none was created or destroyed. Otherwise he would not be able to measure the equivalent of the first in terms of the second force.

Joule had also added to the list of forces that were correlated or convertible. At the time of his writing, 1847, Oersted had shown that electricity could be converted into magnetism and Faraday had found how to convert magnetism into electricity. Joule had converted electricity to heat. He was not the first to perform this conversion, but he established the relationship between heat, electric current, and electric resistance. By concatenating conversions, mechanical force to electric to heat, he was able to calculate the mechanical equivalent of heat. Joule had also performed some experiments that showed that fluid motion, for instance, the passage of water through tubes, could also produce heat. The convertibility of energy may not prove to be a universal rule of nature but it happened often enough to cause men to begin to think of all energy as related. The so-called imponderables, caloric and electric fluid, were not unique substances, it seemed, but different *forms* of one thing, energy.

Later in the century a name-calling type of international scientific dispute was to run for page after page in the journals and in speeches. One of the disputed points was Joule's claim to priority in his researches on heat. But in the 1840's, when he first advocated his ideas, Joule said that "the subject did not excite much general attention." At the 1847 meeting of the British Association for the Advancement of Science, the chairman suggested that Joule not read his paper but confine his remarks to a brief description of his experiments. The paper would have passed without comment, Joule said, "if a young man had not risen in the section and by his intelligent observations created a lively interest in the new theory."

According to the "young man," William Thomson, when he heard Joule's paper he "felt strongly impelled to rise and say that it must be wrong. . . . But as I listened on and on I saw that . . . Joule had certainly a great truth and a great discovery. . . ."[18] At the time, Thomson was deeply involved in thinking out the consequences of Sadi Carnot's work, which was, in 1847, considered by most scientists as the starting point for fruitful work on heat.

Thomson developed the idea of an absolute temperature scale

in a paper, "On an Absolute Thermometric Scale Founded on Carnot's Theory of the Motive Power of Heat. . . .", which was published in the *Philosophical Magazine* in 1848. Thermometers are based upon the characteristic of heat that expands substances when the temperature rises. The distance of the thermometer between degrees depends on the substance used in the thermometer. Some substances gave fairly regular divisions on the thermometer scale; the best was the air thermometer. But as Thomson pointed out no matter how definite or accurate one may make the divisions, all temperature readings were referred to some standard scale. What was needed, he believed, was an end to reliance on trying to improve the relative accuracy of the thermometers and instead to base thermometers on an *absolute* scale. Something else besides the expansion of substances would have to be used. In this paper, Thomson proposed that an absolute scale be based on Carnot's theory of the ideal heat engine. According to Carnot's theory, the sole elements involved in the calculation of the mechanical effect of a heat engine (steam or other type) were quantity of heat and temperature difference between the input of the engine and the exhaust. With the quantity of heat fixed, the mechanical effect would be directly proportional to the temperature difference. As Thomson saw it, the way to set degree intervals on an *absolute* temperature scale was to reverse Carnot's reasoning. The temperature unit of his scale was therefore not based on expansion of a substance but on the mechanical effect produced by a quantity of heat falling one temperature unit.

One of Carnot's principles, and one that Thomson accepted in 1848, was that heat was not convertible. "In actual engines for obtaining mechanical effect through the agency of heat," Thomson wrote, "we must consequently look for the source of power, not in an absorption and conversion, but merely in a transmission of heat." Thomson was not, in 1848, convinced of the validity nor aware of the significance of Joule's work on the mechanical equivalent of heat. As part of the introduction to his paper, Thomson wrote: ". . . the conversion of heat (or *caloric*) into mechanical effect is probably impossible, certainly undiscovered." In a footnote, he added: "This opinion seems to be nearly universally held by those who have written on the subject.

A contrary opinion however has been advocated by Mr. Joule of Manchester" who has made some experiments "with magneto-electric machines, seeming to indicate an actual conversion of mechanical effect into caloric."[19]

Thomson probably believed Joule's results to be correct but he was not sure, as the note above indicated, what to make of them. Ideas change slowly, as Thomson was willing to admit. In 1872 he confessed that he had also rejected Ampère's concept of circulating currents as the cause of magnetism. What Thomson was gradually becoming aware of was that Ampère's and Joule's hypotheses were part of a different way of looking at nature. The new approach was to be called by some the "dynamical view." Thomson had adopted this new attitude sometime between 1847 and 1872. As he wrote in 1872: "I did not then know that motion is the very essence of what has been hitherto called matter. At the 1847 meeting of the British Association in Oxford, I learned from Joule the dynamical theory of heat, and was forced to abandon at once many, and gradually from year to year all other, statical preconceptions regarding the ultimate causes of apparently statical phenomena."[20]

Thomson entered into a collaboration with Joule on the thermal properties of gases. They worked cooperatively for seven years. One of Joule's biographers believed that this collaboration prematurely ended Joule's career as a creative scientist. If Joule "had not subordinated his own superior genius to the solution of Thomson's requests, it might have led him to other solitary regions, where it might have made discoveries as great as those it had made in the previously unchartered regions of experimental theory of heat. In his collaboration with Thomson, Joule behaved like a chief experimental assistant, rather than the collaborator of superior genius."[21]

This judgment mistakes the relationship between the experimentalist and the mathematical theorist. Joule had, as a matter of fact, reached the limit of his experimental exploration. When the collaboration with Thomson ended, Joule returned to calculating the mechanical equivalent of heat in order to make it more accurate. Thomson took up the study of heat where Joule had left off. Fourier was right. Mathematics was essential for forming generalizations from experimental data.

What is heat? Had all of the discussion and research of the first half of the nineteenth century settled this question? By 1850 that question did not seem to matter as much as it did in 1800. Thomson had a paper in the *Philosophical Magazine* in 1852 titled, "On the Dynamical Theory of Heat. . . ." which quickly disposed of the question of the materiality of heat. "Considering it as thus established," he wrote at the beginning of the second page, "that heat is not a substance, but a dynamical form of mechanical effect, we perceive that there must be an equivalence between mechanical work and heat, as between cause and effect."

A new science had begun, that of thermodynamics, which deals with the relationship between heat and mechanical motion and the conversion of one into the other. It was much more fruitful and useful to consider heat in its relation to mechanical motion. Carnot had been the first to see the benefits of studying this relationship. He had used an analogy with the waterwheel and had assumed that just as there was no loss of water as it passed through a waterwheel, so there was no loss of heat when steam passed from a higher temperature to a lower one in driving a steam engine. But Joule insisted that mechanical motion was obtained only when heat was converted to mechanical action. There was no contradiction between the two hypotheses as Thomson and others began to see. One had only to put the two together in order to see the steam engine from the point of view of thermodynamics. Heat passed from a higher level to a lower temperature in order to drive a steam engine, as Carnot had said; but after driving the engine there was less heat, as Joule said, because some of it had been converted into mechanical motion. Heat was not a substance like water, it was a form of energy.

Thus, with the help of Carnot's ideal steam engine and Joule's experimental electric generator, scientists were beginning to perceive heat from an entirely new viewpoint. For many there was a wrench to the imagination, but once it had been accomplished it was difficult to think about heat any other way. Testimony as to the change that had taken place in thinking was the dispute that arose over priority. Some claimed that the German, Julius Mayer, had been the first to state the equivalence between heat and mechanical motion in a paper that he published in 1842. In a general discussion, without the use of experiment or calculation, Mayer said that forces were causes which were *"indestructible, convertible imponderable objects,"* and he posed, but did not solve, the problem of determining "How great is the quantity of heat which corresponds to a given quantity of motion or falling force?"[22]

One year later, 1843, Joule was saying that "the grand agents of nature are, by the Creator's fiat, *indestructible.*" On the basis of this unproven and unprovable postulate, Joule calculated the "mechanical equivalent of heat." These two men, Joule and Mayer, were each hailed by their more chauvinistic countrymen as the true discoverers of the convertibility between heat and mechanical motion. Others were nominated for the role of pioneer in the new field. Thomson in his 1852 paper put forward Justus Liebig's name. "Various statements regarding animal heat, and the heat of combustion and chemical combination, are made in the writings of Liebig . . .", Thomson wrote, "which virtually imply the convertibility of heat into mechanical effect, and which are inconsistent with any other than the dynamical theory of heat."[23]

The key to the controversy over priority is in Thomson's innocent introduction of the words *"virtually imply* the convertibility of heat into mechanical effect." Mayer had made a general suggestion, Joule had based his statement on a strong *a priori* belief, and Liebig's words "virtually imply." To the men of the mid-nineteenth century who had begun to think about heat from the point of view of thermodynamics these suggestions and implications took on significance. The controversy may say something about simultaneity in scientific discovery, but the claims and the counterclaims tell us much more clearly that thermodynamics as a way of viewing nature was well established.

A new science must have beliefs or *a priori* postulates which serve as a foundation for further investigation. These are not and cannot be proven, but they must be accepted before work can proceed. Euclid's geometry was probably the first to introduce postulates. The study of mechanics as approached in the Middle Ages began with the postulate of the impossibility of perpetual motion, a fondly held belief not easily or quickly abandoned.

Chemistry became a science when Lavoisier introduced and worked from the postulate of the indestructibility of matter.

The first law of thermodynamics, which is a postulate, states that when heat is converted to other kinds of energy, the total energy remains constant. The acceptance of this belief, which was accepted *a priori*, has been rightly hailed as the cornerstone of thermodynamics. The law has also been called the most important discovery of the nineteenth century. Yet this first law, the conservation of energy, is a postulate, not a discovery, but because it was accepted as true, thermodynamics was able to move in entirely new and useful directions.

More than one person has been given credit for the statement of the second law of thermodynamics. Two have top priority: Rudolph Clausius and William Thomson. Here again the argument was pointless in that the statements were independently conceived and almost simultaneously published. Thomson rejected any claim to priority and said that "the merit of first establishing the proposition upon correct principles is entirely due to Clausius. . . ."[24] Thomson's statement of the law read: *"It is impossible by means of inanimate material agency, to derive mechanical effect from any portion of matter by cooling it below the temperature of the coldest of the surrounding objects."* Thomson said that he arrived at this conclusion by merging ideas first suggested by Joule and Carnot. The second law is sometimes stated as: heat can only flow from a higher temperature to a lower temperature unless acted upon by some outside force.

To the question: is heat an imponderable or the effect of the motion of minute particles? a physicist after 1850 would answer: "I know that it is *not* a material substance. As to what it is, opinions differ but all that I need to know about heat is stated in the two laws of thermodynamics."

Electricity from Magnetism

3   On November 24, 1831, a no longer young (as age is reckoned in science) scientist, Michael Faraday, read a paper to the Royal Society in which he announced that he had obtained "electricity from ordinary magnetism." Faraday said that Ampère's theory regarding the relationship between electric currents and magnetism suggested other links between the two phenomena, because, Faraday believed, "it appeared very extraordinary, that as every electric current was accompanied by a corresponding intensity of magnetic action" conductors placed in a magnetic field did not have any current induced in them.

"These considerations, with their consequence, the hope of obtaining electricity from ordinary magnetism," Faraday told the Society, "have stimulated me at various times to investigate experimentally the inductive effect of electric currents."[1] That statement summarized over six years of effort. He had begun his search in 1824, and dispersed through his diary during the period 1824 to 1831 were descriptions of experiments, each ending with a note, "exhibited no action" or "no effect." Beginning in August, 1831, and extending through that fall, Faraday produced a series of successful experiments by which, he said, he "arrived at positive results."

What is so remarkable is that Faraday should have believed so strongly that there was a converse to Oersted's experiment. Oersted had shown that an electric current produced a magnetic effect, but it certainly did not follow that magnetism should produce an electric effect. Implicit in Faraday's conviction was the idea of convertibility of energy, which led to the first law of thermodynamics, the conservation of energy. But these were later developments, and Faraday's discovery of the induction of electricity was to be supporting evidence for Joule's work in the 1840's on equivalents.

How does a scientist arrive at a conviction from which he starts an investigation? Is it "intuition," "insight," or something so uncommon that the rest of us cannot imagine what it is like? Faraday took up the search, he said, because given the results of experiments conducted on electricity, it still "appeared unlikely that these could be all the effects induction by currents could produce." Why should there be more? Static electricity produced induction on "an infinity of bodies" while "electricity in motion" could not be made to produce induction. Faraday's starting point, then, was the same as Ampère's, but whereas Ampère had sought a mechanical effect of current electricity similar to that of static electricity, Faraday was seeking an inductive effect of electric currents similar to that produced by static electricity.

Why should Faraday have been the one to be successful in this search where others like Ampère and Arago had failed? He had said that only an experimenter could have made the discovery. What Faraday called the mathematical mind "could not discover dynamic-electricity, nor electro-magnetism, nor magneto-electricity, or even suggest them; though once discovered by the experimentalist," the mathematician can take these subjects up "with extreme facility." Faraday spoke with assurance about the scientific ability of the nonmathematician. "I do not perceive," he wrote, "that a mathematical mind, simply as such, has any advantage over an equally acute mind not mathematical in perceiving the nature and power of a natural principle of action."[2]

Was this Faraday's retort to those scientists who considered experimentalists no more than technicians who puttered in a laboratory? Maxwell, an unstinting admirer of Faraday and his technique, explained Faraday's originality in electrical theory as partly due to a handicap. "Thus Faraday . . . was debarred from following the course of thought which had led to the achievements of the French philosophers," Maxwell wrote, "and was obliged to explain the phenomena to himself by means of a symbolism which he could understand. . . ."[3]

But an experimentalist is not a beachcomber on the shores of science who randomly turns up discoveries like so many pretty colored shells. An experimentalist is a scientist with a strong physical sense. Some men, in science and other fields, conceive of their ideas in words, and others find their intellectual stimulation in, and can work better with, mathematical symbols. The experimentalist deals as much in symbols as the literary and mathematical thinker. The experimentalist, when he tries to portray nature to himself, deals in artificial constructs which are not nature itself but nature synthesized. When an experimenter such as Faraday used wires, batteries, and a galvanometer, the result was as much an abstraction of nature as words are or mathematical symbols.

Both mathematicians and experimentalists used analogy as a mode of advancing new ideas. Sadi Carnot had constructed a mathematical theory of heat, for example, with the aid of an analogy between the flow of heat and water. In Faraday's case the analogy that he used with electricity seems to have come from chemistry. His idea that there must be a "state" that produces change was a chemist's view that such states are a prerequisite for change. Faraday was a self-educated experimental chemist when he began the study of electricity, and it was from this reservoir of experience that he created new ideas in electricity.

Michael Faraday was born in 1791 near London. His father was a blacksmith whose earnings were meagre enough to make him known as a man of "modest means." As a result, Faraday's formal schooling was brief. It ended at thirteen when he became errand boy and then apprentice to a bookbinder. Up to that age he had learned, he said, "little more than the rudiments of reading, writing, and arithmetic at a common day-school." His self-directed education followed an ardent interest in science. He

attended public lectures in natural philosophy and maintained
that he was especially indebted to a Mrs. Marcet's book, *Conversations in Chemistry*. His eagerness and conscientiousness impressed Humphry Davy enough for Davy to take Faraday on as
a laboratory assistant at the Royal Institution in 1813. Soon after
this Davy went on a two year tour of the Continent and Faraday
went along as a combination amanuensis and valet.

The trip to the Continent was a combination honeymoon and
scientific prospecting expedition for Davy. He carried along some
laboratory equipment with which he conducted experiments
wherever and whenever possible. While in France, Davy heard
of a new substance which he analyzed and which he named
iodine. As Faraday wrote to a friend, Davy "goes on discovering."
The international status of science was demonstrated by the fact
that Davy and his party were able to tour France and to be
welcomed in Paris by the leading French scientists while France
and England were at war.

While the trip was for Davy, an established scientist, a means
of stimulating activity into new areas of science, for Faraday the
trip was an education. The liberalizing effect on the young man
can be seen in the letters, filled with expressions of amazement,
that he sent home. Faraday was working on the trip as laboratory
assistant to Davy and by reason of Davy's reputation, Faraday
was able to meet the most distinguished scientists of Europe.
Davy and he carried on scientific discussions with such notables
as Ampère, Gay-Lussac, and Volta. The trip included visits to
France, Italy, Switzerland, and Germany. It lasted a year and a
half, and we can be certain that Faraday was no longer "green"
either socially or scientifically when the group returned to England.

Faraday's first publication was an analysis of caustic lime which
he had brought back from Tuscany. The paper appeared in the
Quarterly Journal of Science in 1816. Faraday was following
Davy in a career in chemistry and the younger man rapidly made
his own reputation. Faraday's first paper in the *Philosophical
Transactions* was published in 1820 and was titled, "On two New
Compounds of Chlorine and Carbon, and on a New Compound
of Iodine, Carbon, and Hydrogen."

Even though Faraday's reputation and place in history came

from his work in electricity, a considerable amount of time and effort in his career was devoted to chemical studies. His achievement in chemistry was, without doubt, appreciable. He succeeded in liquefying a number of gases that had up to that time been considered permanent gases. His work in this area resulted in new concepts of gases, so that it eventually became an accepted idea that all gases were only one state of a substance.

In 1821 Faraday performed original experiments on electromagnetism, vaporized mercury at common temperatures, and in collaboration with someone else developed some unusual alloys of steel. One of the alloys of steel that he developed was closely related to stainless steel. He often gave razors made of this steel to his friends. He was dogged in his pursuit of information in areas that caught his interest and at the same time was broad in the number of things that he undertook.

Faraday gave the Bakerian Lecture before the Royal Society in 1829. His topic was "On the Manufacture of Glass for Optical Purposes." The Bakerian Lecture was one form of recognition received by Faraday in this period. He was elected a Fellow of the Royal Society in 1824 over the objections of Davy. Davy apparently was disturbed by the question of originality of some of Faraday's work. (Was there jealousy too?) With a show of inconsistency, or in an attempt to make amends, Davy recommended Faraday for the post of director of the laboratory at the Royal Institution in 1825. Faraday was appointed Fullerton Professor of Chemistry for life in 1833. The post relieved him of any responsibility for lecturing. Faraday was an exceptionally good lecturer who took his work seriously and evidently enjoyed it. He inaugurated a series of lectures at the Royal Institution known as the Discourses and in his effective efforts to diffuse science, he introduced the Christmas Courses of Lectures for juveniles. He was able to start these lecture series at a time when he was diligently pursuing a career in experimental science. The lecture series was undertaken before he had made his most important contributions to science in electrical theory. Yet in 1833 when he had finished the most important and probably the most taxing part of his experimental work, he was relieved of his duties as lecturer by being made Fullerton Professor in order to pursue experimental work full time. This appointment was another case of the inherent irony in granting recognition for the achievement of a scholar.

Faraday, like so many other scientists of that time, was attracted to the study of electricity by the news of Oersted's and Ampère's work on current electricity. Faraday began with a minor technical success. He succeeded in 1821 in producing rotary motion between a bar magnet and a conductor carrying current. He returned to the subject again in December, 1824. The experiment he conducted then, he expected, would show that "current passing through a wire would be affected by the approach of a strong magnet," but he "could not perceive any effects of this kind." Faraday returned time after time to the same idea and he still continued to experiment and publish the results of his chemical research. Success came in August, 1831. Faraday's diary contains the entry, "Expts. on the production of Electricity from Magnetism, etc. etc."

The report of the success in inducing electricity became what was labeled the "First Series" of his articles that were republished from the *Philosophical Transactions.* All of the "series" were bound together in three volumes entitled *Experimental Researches in Electricity.* The paragraphs were numbered consecutively beginning with the paper published in 1832 and ending with paragraph number 3362, which was published in 1855. In the preface to the *Experimental Researches,* Faraday asked his readers to do him the justice to remember that the articles were "not written as a *whole,* but in parts; the earlier portions rarely having any known relation at the time to those which might follow." Faraday then expressed "great satisfaction" that the parts, which were written over a period of many years (the first volume covered seven years of research), should "harmonize so well as they do." What seemed so surprising to Faraday was that the harmony existed even though the overall plan had not been decided beforehand. "But each professes to contain something of original discovery. . .", he wrote, "it does surprise even my partiality, that they should have the degree of consistency . . . which they seem to me to present." To Whewell reading the *Experimental Researches,* Faraday "appears to have had the consciousness that he was engaged on a great connected work." But Faraday's Preface denied any such consciousness.

The discovery that Faraday made in August of 1831 was that current electricity could induce an electrical effect (a current) in a nearby wire. He might have stopped with this one important fact and been certain that he would be hailed by the scientific world. After all, Oersted's discovery of the magnetic effect of electricity was no more important to scientific theory than Faraday's discovery of that summer. But Faraday pursued the phenomena. During ten days of experiment stretching over the fall months, Faraday not only determined the variety of ways that electricity could be induced but he reduced the whole phenomena to a set of minimum requirements, that is, to its essence. The first experiment was conducted with two coils of wire wrapped around an iron ring. He showed that the ring was not essential by next winding coils on a wooden form. He used permanent magnets as his source of magnetism to show that electrically produced magnetism was not the essential.

Change was the key. He originally found that opening and closing the switch, which opened and closed the circuit in one of the coiled circuits, induced electricity. But he showed that making and breaking the magnetic circuit formed by bar magnets also produced the desired effect, and also that merely moving the bar magnet relative to a coil was an equivalent action. Faraday rotated a copper disc within a magnetic field and noted that induction was produced by moving a conductor, the disc, relative to a magnetic field. The essential of the whole phenomena was relative motion between a magnetic field and a conductor. On the tenth day Faraday found that by merely moving a copper wire between the poles of a horseshoe magnet that he was able to induce a current in the wire.

Many authors have pointed out that during his ten days of experiment Faraday had worked out the essential ideas for the electric generator. Faraday observed that the copper disc was a new electrical machine. He did not follow this line up and try to produce a "more powerful current" because, he said, "I have rather, however, been desirous of discovering new facts and new relations." This desire was what made Faraday an uncommon experimentalist. He was not satisfied, in this case, with having discovered a new phenomena but wanted to find the cause. The theory that he developed was bound to have an aspect of the experimentalist and of a man with considerable experience in chemistry. Faraday's way of conceiving of the phenomena not only affected the development of electrical theory for the rest of the century but it has remained the clearest method of imagining the phenomena of electricity and magnetism ever devised.

Faraday had begun with the hope of producing electricity from magnetism and what he apparently had in mind was an inductive effect similar to that produced by a statically charged body. Yet what he had found was that the making and breaking of an electric circuit or the making and breaking of a magnetic circuit was a new kind of inductive effect. Where lay the difference? It appears that Faraday borrowed an idea from chemistry; the idea was the concept of "state." Faraday had shown by his experiments on liquefying gases that substances hitherto believed to exist in only the gaseous form could exist either as liquid or gas. What accounted for the different characteristics of a substance when it was a gas as compared to its liquid condition was a difference of "state."

"Whilst the wire is subject to . . . volta-electric . . . induction," Faraday mused, "it appears to be in a peculiar state. . . ." For Faraday there was something singular about electric induction. He said that "this electrical condition of matter has not hitherto been recognized, but it probably exerts a very important influence in many if not most of the phenomena produced by currents of electricity." After seeking advice from others Faraday decided to call this electrical condition of matter the *"electro-tonic* state."[4]

The analogy between an electrical condition of matter (the electro-tonic state) and the physical condition of matter (solid, liquid, or gas) can be found in the reasons given by Faraday for arriving at this conclusion. The *Experimental Researches* are a record of Faraday's evolution in thinking. The *Researches,* as Maxwell found out, are also an ideal method of introducing a novice to the study of electricity. True, Faraday never explicitly refers to the use of analogy between chemistry and electricity, but there is further evidence of its use in a letter to his friend in 1831. "Electricity in currents, therefore, exerts an inductive action like ordinary electricity [static electricity], but subject to peculiar laws," he wrote. "The effects are a current in the same direction when induction is established, a reverse current when the induction ceases, and a *peculiar state* in the interim."[5]

Faraday's coining of a new word, *electro-tonic*, was typical of his method. In collaboration with Whewell, Faraday coined a whole new vocabulary of terms for use in electrochemistry, terms like *anode, cathode, electrolyte,* which are still in use. Evidently Faraday was not attempting to manufacture jargon but to develop what has been called a "neutral terminology" which would not bind him to any previous theory.

Further on in the 1831 paper, Faraday attempted to describe a law for the direction of the induced current. He found this law "very simple, although rather difficult to express" and in his effort to express it, he resorted to an illustration of a wire cutting "magnetic curves." He defined these curves as "lines of magnetic forces . . . which would be depicted by iron filings. . . ."[6] Here was the first mention of what finally became known as magnetic lines of force. The lines of force eventually replaced the idea of the electro-tonic state (see article 242 in *Experimental Researches*).

The first sentence of Faraday's *Experimental Researches* was a definition of induction. It was a term to which he returned again and again in his writing because, as he wrote, it was of "the utmost generality in electric action." The transmission of this force by induction could be, and often was, across a space. Just as he was sure that induction represented an almost universal aspect of all electrical phenomena, so he was also sure that induction required a medium, a "third member," as Maxwell said, to be able to transmit the electrical force. Action-at-a-distance as conceived by mathematicians like Ampère was inconceivable to Faraday, who only saw force as the result of action of one body upon another. He had experimental corroboration of this idea when he found that the force exerted between two charged bodies varied according to the substance that was placed between them. The influence of this intervening medium confirmed Faraday's presupposition against action-at-a-distance. For the intervening medium, Faraday coined the word *dielectric*. He said, "I use the word *dielectric* to express that substance through or across which the electric forces are acting."[7]

Faraday's electrical theories were given considerable weight by his contemporaries. His discovery of electromagnetic induction was the most important of a long series of fundamental and striking discoveries in electricity and magnetism. One such discovery might have been the result of a happy chance, but many scientists agreed with Helmholtz's view that "it would be against all rules of probability that a numerous series of the most important discoveries . . . could have had their origin in conceptions which did not really contain a correct, though perhaps deeply hidden, ground of truth."

What Helmholtz meant by "deeply hidden" was that he, along with many other European scientists, had great difficulty in understanding what Faraday meant by such things as "lines of force" and "dielectric." Helmholtz told how he often found himself "despairingly staring" at Faraday's descriptions of lines of force.[8] By mid-century, it was known that electricity produced magnetism, magnetism could produce electricity, a static charge could induce a charge in another body, a current could induce a current in another wire, electricity produced chemical change (electrolysis), and, finally, Faraday had found that magnetism affected light. The number and variety of relationships involving static electricity, current electricity, and magnetism had shown all theories, including Faraday's, to be not comprehensive enough. That, at least, was James Clerk Maxwell's feeling when he began the study of electricity in 1854.

The True Elements
of Bodies

4 It was the nineteenth century's view that science was the description of the forces of change in nature. As William Thomson told his students in the introductory lecture to his course on natural philosophy: "The fundamental subject of Natural Philosophy (science) is dynamics, or the *science of force*," and here he made a note for himself to illustrate this point by explaining light, heat, and chemical change.[1]

Was Thomson correct in associating chemical change with the phenomena of light and heat? James Clerk Maxwell took somewhat of a different view. In an *Encyclopedia Britannica* article on the "Atom" he distinguished between those who used "purely chemical reasoning" and those who applied "dynamical reasoning."[2]

Two ideas, the effort to describe the force behind chemical combination and the attempt to determine the exact composition of substances, were the animation for chemical science during the nineteenth century.

In the eighteenth century Antoine Laurent Lavoisier found a key for making the study of the composition of matter, chemistry, a descriptive discipline. Lavoisier's contribution was to make the study of the composition of matter a quantitative discipline by measuring the weight of substances before and after a reaction. He directed his attention to the reactions of breathing, tarnishing, and combustion. His work was based on the postulate of the conservation of matter, or, what goes into a reaction must come out.

Before Lavoisier, alchemists pursued the inner secret of mystical forces of change. There was the elixir of life, which had the power to prolong life indefinitely. The philosopher's stone, when found, would miraculously transform base metals into gold. What was produced out of this mysticism was an explanation for breathing, tarnishing, and combustion which used an imponderable substance, phlogiston. Phlogiston, being an imponderable, did not obey natural laws and it could in no way be detected or further described.

It was Lavoisier's suggestion that the phenomena of breathing, tarnishing, and combustion did not have a mysterious substance in common, but were chemical reactions involving measurable constituents. The constituent in common with these reactions was also a component of all acids and was called *oxygen*.

For those chemists who accepted Lavoisier's belief in the conservation of matter the primary piece of laboratory equipment became the scale or balance. There were some who continued to maintain that the forces of combination were a useful and necessary subject of study.

On the ninth of Messidor of the year VII (July, 1799) of the French revolutionary calendar, Claude Louis Berthollet read a paper, "Researches into the Laws of Chemical Affinity." This paper contained the first statement of a theory which was to bolster the idea of force in chemical combination. It was an idea that obtained considerable support during the first part of the nineteenth century.

Berthollet, who was born in 1748, received training in chemistry in addition to his medical education. His earliest work was a collaboration with Lavoisier and others to revise chemical nomenclature, which was a fundamental contribution to science. The new nomenclature appeared in 1787. Most of Berthollet's career was associated in one way or another with the French Revolution. For a while he held the post of director of the dyeing industry of France and during that time introduced a new substance (later named *chlorine*) as a bleaching agent. When the revolutionary leaders established the *Ecole Polytechnique,* Berthollet was on the original faculty. He accompanied Napoleon on his expedition to Egypt, and as a member of the Institute of Egypt, Berthollet gave the paper mentioned above in Cairo.

The ideas first suggested by Berthollet in July, 1799, were later published as a volume titled *Researches Respecting the Laws of Affinity,* an abstract of which appeared in the *Philosophical Magazine* in 1801. An extended version was published in 1803 in two volumes titled *Essay on Chemical Statics.*

The object of these works was to outline a general theory of the cause of chemical combination. The attractive power that produced combinations was called *affinity* to distinguish it from the other attractive force between bodies called *gravitational attraction.* Berthollet ventured that it was "probable that each is only the same property. . . ." Since affinity was, he believed, a universal force and similar to, if not identical with, gravitation, affinity should be subject to general laws. The difficulty up to that time was that each chemical reaction seemed to occur under different conditions which were difficult to categorize. But affinity should be subject to general laws just as mechanics was and, he wrote, "it is natural to think" that as chemical principles become more general, "the more they have analogy with those of mechanics. . . ."

"All substances which tend to enter in combination act by reason of their affinity and their quantity. These truths are the basis of all chemical observations." The quantity of a substance, according to Berthollet, could "make up for the force of affinity." How much like Newton's equation of force is Berthollet's "the absolute weight of any body, multiplied by the degree of its affinity, constitutes its mass."[3]

In order to study the principle forces involved in chemical combination and to be able to discover the general laws of combination, Berthollet decided to study the reaction between acids and alkalis "because they act with a force so great as to make the influence of little causes disappear . . . and because they give results easy to be observed."[4] By selecting acids and alkalis as being representative of all chemical combinations, Berthollet was led to conclude that substances combine in varying proportions. Since an acid and an alkali in combination produced an unlimited variety of states of acidity and alkalinity, depending on the strength and quantity of each, it followed that a combination of any two elements would produce the same unlimited variety of compounds. Each of the resulting compounds would have varying amounts of each of the elements.

The general principles that Berthollet chose were the force of affinity and the "mass," or quantity, of substances entering into chemical combination. The experiments that he performed on acids and alkalis indicated a varying power of neutralization. He concluded that all substances had varying degrees of affinity for each other and they combined in varying quantities. Reasoning on the basis of force being the determining factor and quantity a dependent factor, Berthollet had concluded that substances combined in varying proportions by weight.

A strong and effective dissent was entered against this last proposition by another Frenchman, Joseph Louis Proust, who was born in 1754. He followed the more usual path leading to work in chemical research. He was trained as a pharmacist and after a period as a hospital pharmacist in France, he moved to Spain where he became a professor of chemistry at several different universities in turn. His major experimental work was done in Spain.

Proust supported a hypothesis that substances always combine in the same proportion, by weight, in forming specific compounds. This hypothesis was known as *the rule of definite proportions.* Proust based his argument on the belief in the constancy of nature. He determined the composition by weight of many different compounds by carefully conducted experiments. "We must conclude," he wrote in 1799, "that nature operates not otherwise in the depths of the world than at its surface or in the hands of man." This constancy of nature produced compounds of unalterable composition—by weight. "These ever-invariable proportions, these constant attributes, which characterize true compounds of art or of nature. . .", Proust concluded, "is no more at the power of the chemist than the law of election which presides at all combinations."

Proust was interested in measuring the results of chemical

combination and did not concern himself with the forces that produced the combination. Could man know and measure the cause of chemical actions? Not according to Proust, who wrote that "we must recognize that invisible hand which holds the balance for us in the formation of compounds and fashions properties according to its will."[5]

By accepting the relatively narrow and specific rule as written by Proust and supported by many others, chemistry was to continue as the study of composition only. It was to be a system of classification. What makes Berthollet appear out of place in the group of chemical scientists of the early nineteenth century was that he unhesitatingly made grand generalizations because he believed that the analogy with physics gave these generalizations adequate support. The majority of the chemists felt that much more fact gathering was necessary.

The controversy, headed by Berthollet on the one side and Proust on the other, lasted from about 1799 to 1808. It ended because another theory, the atomic theory, dovetailed nicely with the law of definite proportions and thereby lent the law enough support to swing the balance of opinion in its favor.

The belief that matter is made up of minute and indivisible particles (atoms) dates from at least the fifth century B.C., when the Greek, Democritus, postulated the idea. The theory is both ancient and recurring. It cropped up in Roman times, the Middle Ages, and was used by Newton. Each time the idea of atoms was revived, the atoms acquired new aspects. In the eighteenth century a Jesuit priest, Roger Boscovich, wrote *A Theory of Natural Philosophy* in which he used the concept of the atom as a means of reducing to a single law *The Actions Existing in Nature*. John Dalton revived the atomic idea for a new and, as it turned out, provocative theory for the study of chemistry.

Dalton, who was born in 1766, ended his formal education at the age of eleven, "at which time he had gone through a course of mensuration, surveying, navigation, etc." At twelve he taught at a village school and at fifteen became an assistant at a boarding school. In four years he became principal of the boarding school and found time to study Latin, Greek, French, mathematics, and natural philosophy. Dalton became a tutor in mathematics and science at the New College at Manchester in

1793 where he taught for six years. At the end of that time he resigned his post and earned his living by tutoring privately.

Dalton's first efforts (1787) in science were meteorological observations prompted, his biographer wrote, by "his birth and early residence among the lakes and mountains of Cumberland, a region peculiarly exposed to sudden and impressive atmospheric changes. . . ." Dalton made his own instruments and "during the twelve following years, he was satisfied with patiently observing and methodically recording these atmospheric states . . . the relation of air to moisture, was the first to attract his scrutiny, as a question of high theoretical import."[6]

Dalton was a teacher by profession and a scientist by avocation, although the term "natural philosopher" seems more apt. His first attention was given to meteorology but he also observed and collected specimens of caterpillars, snails, mites, and ichneumon flies. At one time he considered changing his profession to medicine. His medical interest led him to conduct experiments on himself to determine weight lost by insensible perspiration. The pursuit of medicine went no further probably because Dalton agreed with his uncle who believed that medicine was "totally out of the reach of a person in thy circumstances."[7]

Dalton did not devote any time to chemistry until 1796. After attending a series of lectures on chemistry in that year, Dalton gave a course of chemistry lectures at his school. He also began to do experiments on his own.

This background, self-taught teacher and amateur scientist, does not presage a man who was to be the start of a revolution in chemistry. There were aspects of Dalton's character that mask any image of a personality inclined towards revolution. He was cautious with a good amount of perseverance, as can be seen by his twelve year stint of day to day notation of atmospheric conditions before he announced his theory of water vapor. In 1799, after the twelve years of work, he "rose from the rank of a servant to that of an interpreter of nature."

If one is to rely on the judgment of the friend and biographer of Dalton, he was "not great in experimental chemistry" in comparison with contemporaries like Davy, Gay-Lussac, or Berzelius. ". . . We cannot hesitate to admit," the writer stated, "Dalton's vast inferiority in experimental chemistry." One of Dalton's papers read in 1813 was described by the same writer as "scarcely on a level with the chemical knowledge of the day. . . ." As an explanation of this shortcoming we are told that "Dalton never possessed the refined instruments, nor had he the manual dexterity, or the mental habitudes or temperament, essential to rigorous experimental determinations."[8]

But let us not be misled into undervaluing Dalton's contribution to science. Humphry Davy voiced the opinion of the day when presenting Dalton with a Royal Society medal in 1826. Davy said:

> Mr. Dalton's permanent reputation will rest upon his having discovered a simple principle, universally applicable to the facts of chemistry . . . and thus laying the foundation for future labours. . . . His merits in this respect resemble those of Kepler in astronomy.[9]

The comparison with Kepler was an apt one. Neither Kepler nor Dalton is remembered for his experimental work. Each man had a fertile idea, which, interestingly, he did not consider of primary importance at first. The fertile ideas became the basis for an advance in science that was remarkable for its extensiveness. Kepler and Dalton therefore derived fame and remembrance not because what they did was the result of a high degree of ingenuity but because what they did produced a spurt of intellectual achievement in *others*. They are remembered for what they provoked more so than for their skill in making the discovery. There is nothing unusual in this outcome. It is eminently historical. Posterity does not care how difficult it was to make a discovery—only how important the results were. Had Columbus made a more daring and difficult trip to the North Pole, he would not be the object of parades and statues today.

It is unusual to find as important a theory as Dalton's atomic theory being advanced with such little experimental support. The answer appears to be that acceptance of a new theory is the joint result of supporting evidence and the readiness of other scientists to be convinced. The scientists of the day were searching, as Davy put it, for a "simple principle, universally applicable to the facts of chemistry."

Dalton first adopted the ancient idea of indivisible particles to explain his meteorological findings. In 1801 he wrote a paper "On the Constitution of Mixed Gases." In this paper he spoke of the repulsive power of "particles" to explain "the *manner* in which mixed elastic fluids [gases] exist together. . . ."[10] The plate with which he illustrated the paper showed each of the different gases that made up the atmosphere represented by symbols. But this was a physical, not a chemical, concept. It was an application of Newton's physics and also his atomic theory. Newton had said that "God in the beginning formed matter in solid, massy, hard, impenetrable, moveable particles, of such sizes and figures, and with such other properties, and in such proportion to space as most conduced to the end for which he formed them. . . ."[11]

Dalton turned his attention to the question of the weight of atoms in a paper "On the Absorption of Gases by Water and Other Liquids," read in 1803. Why, he wondered, did not water absorb "its bulk of every kind of gas alike? This question I have duly considered, and though I am not yet able to satisfy myself completely, I am nearly persuaded that the circumstance depends upon the weight and number of the ultimate particles of the several gases."

From a meteorological consideration of the constituent gases of the atmosphere, Dalton had been led to the question of absorption of gases by liquids and at the end of this paper he disclosed that he had begun to prosecute an "entirely new" enquiry. That enquiry was into the question of the weight of the ultimate particles, or atoms.[12] When this paper was printed in 1805, it had appended to it a table of relative weights of atoms which Dalton had computed.

Thomas Thomson, at one time lecturer in chemistry at Edinburgh and later professor of chemistry at Glasgow, visited Dalton at Manchester in August, 1804, where he learned of Dalton's atomic theory. Thomson is usually described as an "enthusiastic" supporter of the new theory and he was in a position to spread the enthusiasm. As a successful author, Thomson gave weight to Dalton's ideas by giving them a prominent place in his book, *A System of Chemistry,* which went into its third edition in 1807. This description of Dalton's atomic theory was the first to be made public. In his book, Thomson wrote that there was no direct means of determining the density of atoms, but added that Dalton "has lately contrived an hypothesis which, if it prove correct, will furnish us with a very simple method of ascertaining that density with great precision."[13]

Thomson was also editor of the *Annals of Philosophy*, a journal devoted to "Chemistry, Minerology, Mechanics, Natural History, Agriculture and the Arts." In its pages, Thomson gave additional support to Dalton's theory by his own writing and through articles submitted by others.

Substantial bolstering for the new theory came from William Hyde Wollaston, who gave a report to the Royal Society in 1808. He had been trying to devise a general theory of chemical combination. "But since the publication of Mr. Dalton's theory . . . the inquiry which I had designed appears to be superfluous," Wollaston said, "as all of the facts that I had observed are but particular instances of the more general observations of Mr. Dalton." Nevertheless, Wollaston revealed his findings of the composition of salts, which confirmed Dalton's view. Wollaston noted, that "the simple elements of bodies are disposed to unite atom to atom singly, or, if either is in excess, it exceeds by a ratio to be expressed by some multiple of the number of its atoms."

Near the end of his talk, Wollaston ventured the thought that an arithmetical conception of atoms would not suffice and "that we shall be obliged to acquire a geometrical conception of their relative arrangement in all the three dimensions of solid extension."[14]

After this advanced information, which smoothed the way, Dalton's version of his atomic theory appeared in the first volume of his *A New System of Chemical Philosophy*, which was published in 1808. Dalton found Berthollet's theory of affinity unacceptable because Berthollet had said that affinity was proportional to mass. Dalton explained how he had started with a different premise. Since a quantity of water always weighed the same regardless of where the sample was obtained, it was apparent that the invariant in all substances was weight. Constant weight then became the starting point for Dalton and if it be conceded that the weight of a particle of water is the same wherever found, then it must follow that its constituents, hydrogen and oxygen, have constant weight. "Therefore we may conclude," Dalton said, "*that the ultimate particles of all homogeneous bodies are perfectly alike in weight, figure, &c.*" The premise supported his contention that "every particle of water is like every other particle of water; every particle of hydrogen is like every other particle of hydrogen, &c. . . ." And this identity was designated by weight. How important the idea of weight was to the atomic theory was emphatically stated by Dalton: "Now it is one great object of this work, to shew the importance and advantage of ascertaining *the relative weights of the ultimate particles* [atoms], *both of simple and compound bodies.* . . ."[15]

Dalton's rule of greatest simplicity was a way of getting around a dilemma. The weight of one element that would combine with the weight of another element to form a compound was known, but to determine the "relative weights of the ultimate particles," one had to know the number of atoms of each element in the compound molecule. Dalton was certain that he knew how to determine this number. When two bodies were "disposed to combine," the rule of greatest simplicity assumed that they would combine one atom to one atom. If these elements formed more than one compound, the combination increased in complexity one step at a time. The second step was one atom with two atoms; the third was two atoms with one atom; and the fourth, one atom with three atoms, and so on up. Without some such assumption there was no way of determining atomic weights. As one chemist wrote, the numbers of atoms of each element in a compound "cannot be *ascertained* in the case of a single chemical compound. They can only be gathered according to grounds of *probability* from various relations and arguments, to be hereafter enumerated," by more experiments.[16]

The atomic theory was widely, although not universally, accepted in 1808. Whether looked on as a calculating model, as some chemists chose to do, or as reality, the theory formed the basis for an approach to the study of chemical combination. The atom to atom concept viewed substances from a still-life point of view. The dynamics of Berthollet was found unsatisfactory, for the time being. The acceptance of the atomic theory did not settle all disputes. Acceptance simply meant that disputes would be fought out on this ground. There still remained the problem of determining the weights of the atoms and the numbers in combination. The rule of greatest simplicity was too simple and too baldly a device with which to avoid a tough question.

The Berthollet-Proust debate had left most chemists convinced of Proust's views on definite proportions of compounds. His experimental evidence was the determining factor. Most chemists thought Berthollet's ideas on affinity too speculative. The law of definite proportions and the law of multiple proportions were seen to be mutually substantiating. Dalton's speculation on the atom to atom linkage "explained" both the definiteness of composition of compounds and why elements always combined in multiples of some basic weight.

A criticism of Dalton's theory appeared in the *Philosophical Transactions* of 1811. The writer remarked that the atomic theory was neither necessary nor useful:

> It is impossible not to admire the ingenuity and talent with which Mr. Dalton has arranged, combined, weighted, measured, and figured his atoms; but it is not, I conceive, on any speculations upon the ultimate particles of matter, that the true theory of definite proportions must ultimately rest.

This mild dissent was written by Humphry Davy, whose inclinations and opportunities led him more in the direction of experimental work. Davy eventually accepted the atomic theory, recognized Dalton's priority, and willingly participated in the bestowal of honors. But Davy always maintained that Dalton's data was more valuable than his theory. "Indeed, in my opinion, Mr. Dalton is too much of an *Atomic Philosopher*," Davy once wrote.[17]

Humphry Davy was born in 1778. He ended his formal schooling when he was fifteen years old and began his self-education. He was apprenticed to a surgeon and apothecary at sixteen. His vocational training led him to the study of chemistry and within a few months he brazenly published, "Essays on Heat, Light, and the Combination of Light, with a New Theory of Respiration."

Critics dealt severely with this work and Davy regretted becoming involved in this kind of speculation, which he thenceforth avoided. Scientists never appear to be able to describe exactly how they distinguish between a speculation and a theory. A theory, all agree, has more evidence to support it than a speculation. But *how* much more? No scientist seems to be willing to say, but all operate on the premise that they can recognize the distinction between speculation and theory when the need arises.

The medical apprenticeship was never completed by Davy. In 1798 he obtained a release in order to accept a position as superintendent at the Pneumatic Institution. The Institution was maintained by subscription from "liberal men of science." It was equipped with a hospital, experimental research laboratory, and a lecture hall. The purpose was to discover the medicinal uses of the different gases. It was an ideal opportunity for Davy.

Davy was energetic and had varied interests. To his notebook he resolved: "To work two hours with pen before breakfast on 'The Lover of Nature;' and 'The Feelings of Eldon,' [a novel] from six till eight; from nine till two, in experiments; from four to six, reading; seven till ten, metaphysical reading (i.e., system of the universe)."[18]

Davy published some papers on nitrous oxide, "the pleasure-producing air," while at the Pneumatic Institution and earned enough of a reputation to prompt an offer from Count Rumford to come to the Royal Institution as a professor of chemistry. This was in 1801.

The position at the Royal Institution offered Davy more time and a more complete laboratory for conducting his experiments. His move occurred at about the same time as Volta's announcement of his new invention, the electric battery. Davy was among the most enthusiastic in his exploration of uses for the battery in chemical analysis. For this particular young man (he was twenty-one when news of the battery reached England), the new apparatus meant fresh opportunity. "Till this discovery, our means were limited," he said later, "the field of pneumatic research had been exhausted, and little remained for the experimentalist except minute and laborious processes. There is now before us a boundless prospect of novelty in science; a country unexplored, but noble and fertile in aspect."[19]

Other scientists shared Davy's enthusiasm, as evidenced by the zeal with which experiments were conducted. Volta's letter announcing his invention was dated March 20, 1800. By the end of the next month Nicholson and Carlisle had constructed a battery and on the second of May, decomposed water. Their success was announced in *Nicholson's Journal* before the formal announcement of Volta's work appeared in the *Philosophical Transactions*. Davy's account of experiments with the "Galvanic Apparatus" was published in *Nicholson's Journal* of September, 1800.

The distinction between the theoretician and the experimentalist was illustrated by Davy's work in the use of the battery in chemical analysis. The relationship between electrical energy and chemical affinity was "sufficiently evident" to him. Yet even after he had achieved considerable success in electrical decomposition, he would not venture a hypothesis. "Hypotheses," he wrote, "can scarcely be considered of any value, excepting as leading to new experiments." To Davy, being right about the relationship between electricity and chemical affinity meant, not that he was on the verge of a new theory, but that he had a powerful new tool for analysis. Electrical attraction of elements had a "natural" limitation but "our artificial instruments [batteries] seem capable of indefinite increase." What was to be hoped for then was "that the new mode of analysis may lead us to the discovery of the *true* elements of bodies. . . ."[20] The combining force was assumed but not studied.

Davy turned his attention to the alkaline earths (among them potash and soda) and by means of some expertly designed experiments, he was able to decompose them and obtain the *true* elements, potassium and sodium. In a short while, muriatic acid surrendered the mystery of its composition. Davy announced to the Royal Society that one of the components of the acid was a hitherto unknown gas, which he named *chlorine*.

Not everyone accepted the claim that chlorine was new or that it was an element. Many insisted that what Davy had isolated was oxymuriatic gas, which was a compound containing oxygen. Davy responded to the demand for "stronger evidence of chlorine being undecompounded" by answering that it was impossible to give more proof since chlorine had "resisted all attempts of decomposition." In that respect, chlorine was like gold, silver, hydrogen, and oxygen. "Persons may doubt, whether these are elementary bodies," was Davy's rejoinder, "but it is not philosophical to doubt, whether they have not been resolved into other forms of matter."[21]

Davy, in his pursuit of facts that could be mined by using the new electrochemical techniques, had jostled a venerable theory. This theory was associated with Berthollet and Lavoisier, who had chosen the name for oxygen, which means "begets acid." According to Davy's finding, muriatic acid consisted of hydrogen and chlorine. There was no oxygen present in this acid and it appeared to be the exception that disproved the oxygen-acid theory.

Some chemists, Dalton among them, maintained their skepticism about Davy's results for quite some time. Experimental findings, like speculations, have always been subject to the scrutiny of doubters. Had he performed the experiments correctly and had he interpreted the results rightly? In 1827, long after most chemists had accepted the fact that chlorine was an element, Dalton could still write: "More experience must be had before all the doubts and difficulties are removed from the subject."[22]

The criticism on the grounds that the findings about chlorine conflicted with theory called for an answer. Davy reminded his audience at the Royal Society in 1814 that chemists in the eighteenth century had hampered themselves by blind adherence to a theory; in their case, it was the phlogiston theory. "It was the glory of Lavoisier to lay the foundations for a sound logic in chemistry," Davy told his audience, "by shewing that the existence of this principle, or of other principles, should not be assumed where they could not be detected."[23] It was wanton obstructionism to reject experimental evidence because it disagreed with a theory, Davy maintained. Actually, it was a question of what to base a judgment on: the well established oxygen-acid theory or Davy's carefully conducted experiments.

A treatise, which is reminiscent of Galileo's polemics, was written to consider the truth about chlorine. The title was an explanation in itself: *Versuch einer Vergleichung der älteren und der neueren Meinungen über die Natur der oxydierten Salzsäure, zur Beurteilung des Vorzuges der einen vor der anderen* (An attempt to compare the Old and New Opinions with regard to the Nature of the Oxidised Muriatic Acid, and to estimate the Advantages of the One over the Other).

The balance of the advantages definitely weighed in favor of the old oxygen-acid theory according to this treatise, which was written by J. J. Berzelius. In the work, Berzelius indicated a theoretician's reluctance to be swayed by experimental disproof of a key theory. He rejected Davy's claim to having discovered an acid that did not contain oxygen. Theory, above all else, must be consistent. "For I demand uncompromisingly," he wrote, "from any chemical theorem that it shall agree with the rest of chemical theory and be capable of incorporation in it; if this be not the case, then I must reject it. . . ." The qualification to this remark showed how firm Berzelius' opposition was: ". . . unless, indeed, the evidence in its favour is of such an incontrovertible nature as to necessitate a revolution in the chemical theory with which it is at variance."[24]

Jöns Jacob Berzelius was born in Sweden in 1779. His original training was in medicine, but he took up a concentrated study of chemistry after being appointed to the faculty of the University of Stockholm. In 1815 he was appointed to the chair of chemistry at the Chirurgio-Medical Institute of Stockholm.

His accomplishments earned him many honors during his lifetime. He became a member of the Stockholm Academy in 1808 and its permanent secretary in 1818. He was elected foreign member of the French Academy of Sciences and of the Royal Society and most of the other scientific societies of the world. In 1835 he was made a baron by the King of Sweden.

Berzelius once wrote that Davy might have been a great chemist but remained only a *glänzendes Bruchstück* (brilliant fragment), "because he was not compelled from the beginning to initiate himself thoroughly into every part of the science as into one organic whole."[25]

Berzelius began his work in a fairly narrow way but he expanded his view until his scope was fully as broad as Berthollet's. Berzelius' first publication, a joint authorship, was in 1803 and it was a paper on some effects of the voltaic battery. No chemist escaped the allure of the battery, which, Davy said, opened a "boundless prospect of novelty."

Berzelius soon ventured to extend his area of interest. He decided that the most important area for chemical research was to determine the atomic weights of as large a number of elements as possible, "and, above all, of the most commonly occurring ones." These, he decided, "must be determined with the greatest accuracy attainable." Berzelius subscribed to Dalton's atomic theory, but he found "Dalton's numbers were wanting in that accuracy which was requisite for the practical application of his theory." Berzelius set about providing the experimental support for Dalton's theory by means of more accurately determined atomic weights. Dalton had thrown a new light on chemical science, but without the more accurate data, Berzelius believed, "no day would follow the morning dawn."

After ten years of careful and unstinting labor, Berzelius was able in 1818 to publish a table of atomic weights for about 2000 elements and compounds.[26]

In an article published in *Annals of Philosophy*, 1813, Berzelius stated his regard for the principles of definite and multiple proportions. These principles pointed to a single cause. "Now *what is that cause?*" he asked. "It is obvious that the answer to that question must constitute the principal basis of chemical theory."[27] Dalton's hypothesis was the first step.

Berzelius was a supporter of the atomic theory from the start, but, as he wrote, he considered it "imperfect" and "full of difficulties." He was pained to find that Dalton considered this probing as criticism. As Berzelius saw it, Dalton and he differed in their approach to truth. Where Dalton was an "inventor" who set "out from a first principle, from which he endeavours to deduce the experimental results," Berzelius saw himself as "obliged to take the road of an ordinary man, collecting together a number of experiments, from which I have endeavoured to draw conclusions more and more general." Berzelius was not claiming that his work was superior to Dalton's; far from it. "I have endeavoured to mount from experiment towards the first principle," he wrote, "while Mr. Dalton descends from that principle to experiment. It is certainly a great homage to the speculations of Dalton if we meet each other on the road."[28]

The comparison between road building and formulating a theory is not a satisfactory one unless one is thinking of building roads into uncharted wilderness. In each case there must be a starting point. For roads there is the bench mark, which is the surveyor's reference point. For theories the bench mark is an idea. Dalton had begun from a meteorological interest in the gases of the atmosphere. The solubility of gases in water arose quite naturally and from these questions he passed to the atomic theory. This theory then opened the way, as he saw it, to further research on the composition of substances. On the other hand, the atomic theory, the idea of atomic weights and of definite proportions, was the beginning point for Berzelius. Contrary to what Berzelius said, both men used experiment as a basis for building theory. Berzelius simply did not see that Dalton had found his bench mark in another area, meteorology, which was across the river, as it were.

Berzelius was not satisfied, as Dalton was, that the atomic theory was complete in itself. Far from considering that theory complete, Berzelius thought it should be the beginning of a more general theory of chemistry. It was the duty of every scientist "to endeavour to reach the first principle of the science" even though this object was unattainable. It was Berzelius' idea that further research into the explanation for the laws of constant and multiple proportions had to be coupled with a search for an answer to why atoms combine at all. His hypothesis was known as the *electrochemical* or *dualistic theory.*

This theory assumed that all substances that entered into a chemical combination had either a positive or negative charge. These opposite charges accounted for chemical affinity, or the tendency of substances to combine. When they combined, the electricity disappeared and there was a rise in temperature that sometimes produced fire in the same manner as the discharge of a Leyden jar or lightning. The contrary of chemical combination was produced by the application of electricity by means of a voltaic pile or battery, such as Davy had performed with great success.

The influence of Berzelius' earlier work, on the voltaic pile, can be seen in his electrochemical theory. He even drew up a table that listed substances in order of their intensities of electricity, beginning with the most negative and passing down to the most positive. The table is the chemical counterpart of Volta's electric series of metals used in the construction of batteries.

Berzelius' electrochemical theory reached its apogee in 1830 and maintained its influence for some years afterwards. Like Berthollet's law of affinity, the electrochemical theory was an attempt to establish a grand generalization for chemistry. Its success can be measured by the controversy it stirred up with a resultant spurt of research which sought either to prove it right or wrong. Berzelius was both what he called an "ordinary man," a collector of experimental facts, and an important figure in theoretical chemistry, that is, someone who "endeavoured to draw conclusions more and more general."

In his work *Essay upon the Theory of Chemical Proportions and upon the Chemical Action of Electricity,* first published in 1814, Berzelius expounded on his version of the atomic theory. Here his dualistic theory was explained and since it was translated from the original Swedish into French and German, the theory achieved a wide audience. This work also contained the result of long and careful labor in determining correct atomic weights. The 2000 substances that he had analyzed were described. For some time the accuracy of these findings was challenged, but for the most part they were correct.

In the same book, Berzelius introduced his new system of chemical nomenclature. The idea was impressive in its simplicity. He proposed to use the first letter of the Latin name of the elements as a means of designation. Each symbol represented an elementary volume, and the addition of numerals enabled him to indicate the composition of compounds. The results of a chemical analysis could then be represented and "as easily remembered, as the algebraic formulas in mechanical philosophy." Some called the new system "horrifying," others referred to its "abominable symbols." The opposition has long since been forgotten. The system is still in use.

Berzelius was not always right. He unsuccessfully opposed the elemental nature of chlorine, the type theory, the substitution theory, and his own dualistic theory fell after a barrage of criticism. Writers were pained when pointing out Berzelius' resort to exaggeration and his unfortunate use of speculation in the attempts to defend his theories. He fought his battles earnestly, but with the politeness of a gentle man. Nevertheless, Berzelius advanced chemistry through his vast number of discoveries and according to one view, "this powerful contradictor has also served it [chemistry] even by his errors."[29]

Berzelius' efforts towards increasing the accuracy of atomic weights and his success in extending the list to 2000 substances were a lasting contribution to chemistry. His formulation of the dualistic theory of chemical combination did provoke a spirited discussion. But for most chemists of the mid-nineteenth century, chemistry stopped with the quantitative measurement of inter-acting substances or what had been labeled "stoichemistry," that is, the measurement of the proportions in which elements combine without regard to forces involved.

Both Berthollet and Berzelius had attempted to form a general theory of chemistry founded on the force involved in chemical combination. Another nineteenth century effort to find a universal in chemistry was made using composition of substances, not the force binding them, as a basis for generalization. In this respect the new theory was like Dalton's, except that the building blocks of nature were reduced from many different atoms to a single component.

William Prout's hypothesis, which was to be the subject of controversy for almost a half century, was presented to the world inauspiciously in a paper titled "Correction of a Mistake in the Essay on the Relation between Specific Gravities of Bodies in their Gaseous State and the Weights of their Atoms," which was published in 1816. Prout, who was born in 1785, was a practicing physician in London at the time he wrote the paper. Prout's calculations of specific gravities of several different gases led him to a simplification which he thought would aid calculation. That simplification was, to consider a volume of hydrogren equal to an atom of hydrogen. With hydrogen as unity he found that all other specific gravities were some multiple of hydrogen.

The next step for Prout was to suggest that perhaps hydrogen was the universal substance that had been the object of a search and of hypothesis since ancient times. If the weight of all substances was some multiple of the atomic weight of hydrogen, then it was not too farfetched to believe that hydrogen was the basic building block in nature. For chemistry, Prout's idea was especially appealing both mathematically and conceptually.

In 1860, a Belgian chemist, Jean Servais Stas, published a paper that maintained that Prout's hypothesis was a "pure" illusion. Stas wrote that any efforts to establish a relationship between elements by weights had proven fruitless. His experiments had reaffirmed the exactness of Berzelius' atomic weights, which contradicted Prout's hypothesis, and Stas declared himself in favor of the experimental method "for determining the laws which regulate matter." The paper concluded with the statement: "The incontestable analogy of properties observed amongst certain elements must be sought in other causes than those originating in the ratio of weight of their reacting masses."[30]

It was true that there was something provoking about the way the properties of different substances almost fell into categories. If there was some underlying unity, it had eluded theorists so far. Many chemists felt the conflict between theories would have to be settled before they would feel safe in postulating further. No more theory building until the foundation was made firm. It was hoped that the hesitancy would disappear once the congress at Karlsruhe had finished deliberating.

Karlsruhe

5   On July 10, 1860, a circular letter signed by forty-five chemists was sent to all European chemists. It began by saying:

> Chemistry has reached a state of development when to the undersigned, it seems necessary that a meeting of a great number of chemists, active in this science, who are called upon to do research and teach, be held so that a unification of a few important points shall be approached.

It was hoped that "more precise definitions of the concepts of atom, molecule, equivalent. . . ." could be agreed upon.[1]

Actually the "state of development" had been reached in 1811. In almost a half century of work gathering information, chemical theory had not reached a state of certainty or unanimity, which was considered essential for an "exact" science.

In a memoir published in 1809, Joseph-Louis Gay-Lussac had analyzed compounds formed from gases in the belief that only substances in the gaseous state exhibit "simple and regular laws." He hoped that by finding the laws of gaseous combination chemistry would be brought closer to "the time when we shall be able to submit the bulk of chemical phenomena to calculation."[2]

The law Gay-Lussac discovered was that gases always combine in proportion to their volumes. These proportions are simple whole numbers; one volume of gas combines with one volume, or two volumes, or at most three volumes of another. This relationship by volume was not characteristic of solids or liquids. According to Gay-Lussac, his findings were consistent with Dalton's atomic theory.

But Dalton disagreed. In the second part of his *New System of Chemical Philosophy,* Dalton specifically repudiated Gay-Lussac's findings. Gay-Lussac's "notion of measure is analogous to mine of atoms," Dalton wrote, "and if it could be proved that all elastic fluids have the same number of atoms in the same volume . . . the two hypotheses would be the same, except that mine is universal, and his applies only to elastic fluids [gases]."[3] Then Dalton, whose experimental technique was vastly inferior to Gay-Lussac's, proceeded to lecture Gay-Lussac on the necessity of accuracy.

Dalton was not alone in his opposition to Gay-Lussac. But it was Amedeo Avogadro who believed that Gay-Lussac had not contradicted, but on the contrary, broadened the Daltonian-atomic theory. Put Gay-Lussac's findings together with Dalton's theory and, Avogadro believed, "it must then be admitted that very simple relations also exist between the volumes of gaseous substances and the number of simple or compound molecules which form them."[4]

One objection to accepting the idea that equal volumes of gases contain equal numbers of molecules was that it did not jibe with experiment. For example, in the formation of water, two volumes of hydrogen combined with one volume of oxygen to form two volumes of water vapor. If equal volumes contained an equal number of particles and the known atomic weights of these particles, of hydrogen and oxygen, were taken into account, the result *should* have been one volume of water vapor. The difficulty, Avogadro insisted, stemmed from the fact that chemists did not distinguish between molecules and atoms (he called them *elementary molecules*). A molecule of hydrogen consists of two atoms (written H_2) and a molecule of oxygen consists of two atoms. Therefore two volumes of hydrogen ($2H_2$) plus one volume of oxygen (O_2) equals two volumes of water vapor ($2H_2O$).[5]

Avogadro's two atom molecules were part of a hypothesis, but he insisted that his hypothesis was acceptable since it agreed both with Dalton's ideas and Gay-Lussac's findings. Avogadro's essay was published in 1811. Ampère, without knowing of Avogadro's work, restated the theory in 1814.

Approximately 140 of the world's leading chemists met at Karlsruhe, the capital of the grand-duchy of Baden, on September 3, 1860. They came from almost every country in Europe in response to that circular letter of the previous July. The meeting lasted three days, and it was their naive hope that they could settle some of the serious differences of opinion on basic ideas that were obstructing research in chemistry (or so they thought) and hindering teaching. The Karlsruhe Congress was a disappointment to those who held such hopes; nevertheless, the outcome of the meeting was fortunate in ways not anticipated by the planners.

The letter of invitation had said that an open forum on these issues "would not be in the position to make definite binding conclusions" but there was reason to hope that "it should be possible by this means at least to prepare the way for a desirable agreement on these important questions."

Not all of the leading protagonists in the chemical debates came, not even all of those who signed the invitation. Was it because the Congress obviously, and by the admission of the invitation, would be too weak to "make definite binding conclusions"? Or did some stay away because they believed, binding or no, that controversies in science could not be settled in congresses?

The greeting to the Congress was delivered by Carl Weltzein, who was professor of chemistry at the Technische Hochschule at Karlsruhe, and manager of the Congress. His address pointed up the historical significance of the meeting:

> For the first time we have here assembled the representatives of a single science and the youngest. The representatives belong to almost all nationalities. We belong to different national groups and speak different languages, but we are united by a scientific interest, by a common intention.

The representatives of this youngest science did not, according to Weltzein, feel that their discipline was an exact one because of the differences of opinion. How unhistorical that feeling was! How little, apparently, they knew of the similar difficulties in the more "exact" science of physics. In the address, Weltżein urged his listeners to consider "the importance of chemistry to other sciences, because of the necessity of a knowledge of chemistry in engineering, it is obviously desirable and essential to give chemistry a more exact formulation so that it will be possible to teach it in a relatively short time."

The stalemate with which the Congress ended indicates that there was not only a difference of opinion of the definitions of the concepts of atom, molecule, and equivalent. Most important to the outcome of the meeting was the weight placed upon these differences. Were they in fact fundamental, or were they of little consequence, as Weltzein thought? He said that chemists "should not be forced to use various opinions and methods of representation wherein the differences are of little importance. . . ."

What was the Congress of Karlsruhe? Was it a meeting where little more had to be done than agree upon uniform measure, such as deciding whether to use metric or English units? Or were the differences of fundamental theoretical nature such that a chemist could only agree to some of the views at the expense of dearly held beliefs? If the first were the case, then there was every reason for optimism; but if the second were the prevalent attitude, there was no hope at all of a concensus.

A committee was appointed to prepare questions that the Congress would discuss and pass upon. The committee had trouble framing questions that were acceptable to all of its members and when they finally reported to the Congress, one of the dissenting members of the committee spoke against the report. The discussion on the floor was a confrontation of opposing opinion, which in itself was useful, but there was not the possibility of a settlement of the disputed points. As the protagonists saw it, the questions *were* fundamental and not as Weltzein had said, "of little importance." One thing all agreed on: the Congress could not force any opinion on the scientists and with this obvious conclusion, the Congress adjourned.

What must have been the feeling of the chemists as they

departed from Karlsruhe in that September of 1860? For those who had high hopes for the Congress, the feeling must have been despondency. On the train home, one chemist, Lothar Meyer, read a pamphlet that had been distributed at the Congress. "It was as though the scales fell from my eyes," was his delighted exclamation, "doubt vanished, and was replaced by a feeling of peaceful certainty."[6] The pamphlet was titled *Sketch of a Course in Chemical Philosophy Given in the Royal University of Genoa.* The pamphlet did for chemical theory what the Congress at Karlsruhe was supposed to do. The disagreement was settled, not by proving one view correct and the other mistaken, but by showing that the two views were, in fact, in agreement. Its impact was profound in spite of the fact that it contained no revolutionary discoveries or news of original experiments. In fact, it was, as the author claimed, only an "historical examination of chemical theories."

The *Sketch for a Course in Chemical Philosophy* was written by Stanislao Cannizzaro, who was professor of chemistry at Genoa. He was born in Palermo, Sicily, in 1826. Cannizzaro was both a political activist and a chemist. He managed to fill these roles simultaneously. Unlike Fourier, who kept politics paramount, Cannizzaro was always first a professor of chemistry. He had been an artillery officer for the Italian revolutionaries in 1848.

He was appointed to the chair of chemistry at the University of Genoa in 1855 and his *Sketch* was first printed in 1858. At the same time, 1860, that the *Sketch* was causing a stir in Karlsruhe, Cannizzaro was involved in planning a political reform in Palermo. In 1871 he was appointed professor of chemistry at the University of Rome and in the same year was made a senator of the kingdom. In this latter role he played a part in the political reorganization of Italy.

Cannizzaro's description of his course in chemistry can be compared with the reports on the recent progress and present state of knowledge in the several fields of science which were annually given to the British Association for the Advancement of Science. In the British Association reports, some recognized leader in science wrote on the development of theories in his field, discussing controversies and usually making a judgment on the worth of each view. Cannizzaro was presumably writing for students, but many chemists who were well beyond the student stage benefited from his clear exposition of the "present state of knowledge" in chemistry. The object of the course was to "lead my students to the conviction which I have reached myself."

He began his *Sketch* by affirming his belief that Avogadro and Ampère's gas law was true; that is, that equal volumes of gases "contain an equal number of molecules: not however an equal number of atoms." Here was an answer to one of the major difficulties at Karlsruhe, where the inability to make a clear distinction between atom and molecule gave trouble. Many obstacles to the collating of the different chemical theories could be avoided by following Cannizzaro's suggestion. Simply take Avogadro and Ampère's law that equal volumes of gases have equal numbers of particles as meaning that these particles were molecules (more than one atom) rather than single atoms. It was remarkably easy to visualize the existence of gas molecules. But there were serious objections to this idea when force between particles was taken into account.

Cannizzaro outlined the development of the Avogadro-Ampère law and showed how it came "almost spontaneously" from Gay-Lussac's law of combining volumes.

"I set myself the task," Cannizzaro wrote, "of investigating the reasons why this hypothesis of Avogadro and Ampère was not immediately accepted by the majority of chemists." The obstacle was Berzelius' ideas, which made the Avogadro-Ampère hypothesis *appear* to be in error. For Berzelius' dualism, where like atoms have the same electric charge, seemed to rule out the possibility of molecules of elements that contained two atoms. Cannizzaro showed how Berzelius was led to more untenable hypotheses by sticking by his dualism. To avoid this trap, Cannizzaro chose to disregard the forces of combination and deal solely with what was combined.

"In the fourth lecture I pass under review the chemical theories since Berzelius." This review by Cannizzaro covered the major figures of chemistry of the first half of the nineteenth century. He covered organic as well as inorganic chemistry and experimental as well as theoretical. He then concluded:

> From the historical examination of chemical theories, as well as from physical researches, I draw the conclusion that to bring into harmony all the branches of chemistry we must have recourse to the complete application of the theory of Avogadro and Ampère in order to compare the weights and the numbers of the molecules. . . .

The sequel contains demonstration after demonstration in the form of tables of weights and volumes to bolster the theories. And towards the end of the course, Cannizzaro reminded his pupils once more that "the theory of Avogadro and Ampère being constantly the guiding thread which leads me in the study of chemical reactions."[7]

The success of Cannizzaro's *Sketch* in winning assent was due to his scheme of generalizing the atomic theory. He showed how Dalton's, Avogadro's, and Gay-Lussac's theories not only did not conflict but supported each other. When they were joined together they presented a clear explanation of substances by using weight and composition. Cannizzaro purposely left out the uncertain and conflicting hypotheses, such as those dealing with the forces of combination, for example, Berzelius' dualism. Cannizzaro showed chemists what was plausible in the way of hypothesis and he declared that if they were willing to adopt these few postulates, then all branches of chemistry came into harmony. He did not prove the Dalton-Avogadro-Gay-Lussac atomic theory. He showed how plausible it was.

Those who called the Congress at Karlsruhe mistakenly believed that the "true" theory would automatically prevail if only it were given a chance. Cannizzaro had a more sensible approach. He showed how one theory was reasonable, plausible, and therefore acceptable. This episode is an example of one use of scientific theory. A theory is a point of view that is invented in order to gain better understanding of phenomena. A theory is not a truth that is discovered. A theory wins adherents by appealing to the imagination. Like Lothar Meyer, many chemists, upon reading Cannizzaro's *Sketch,* found that the scales fell from their eyes and doubt vanished. When there were enough who were convinced, the atomic theory became established. No vote at Karlsruhe would have accomplished the same thing.

One participant in the Congress remembered, years later, "how vain were the hopes of coming to an understanding. . . ." But this chemist, Dmitri Ivanovich Mendeleev, had also been strongly influenced by the meeting. He recalled the impression left on him by Cannizzaro's speeches which "seemed to advocate truth itself." What this encounter enabled Mendeleev to do was part of the aftermath of Karlsruhe.

Nineteenth century chemists were still, as in the Middle Ages, obtaining training in pharmacy or medicine. Examples were Proust, Davy, and Berzelius. But employment opportunities were expanding. Many worked for their governments as special advisers to industries. From Berthollet, who was technical adviser in the French Revolution, to Marcellin Berthelot, who was president of the French Scientific Committee of National Defense which supervised manufacture of explosives during the Franco-Prussian War, the chemists were valuable to governments in war and peace of the new industrial era. All chemists do not fit the pattern and by mid-century the opportunities were so varied that generalization about them is difficult. Dmitri Ivanovich Mendeleev's career was characteristic of this shift in background.

Mendeleev was the youngest of fourteen children. His widowed mother had decided on a scientific career for her youngest, but was unable to get Mendeleev admitted to the university. Instead he was enrolled at the St. Petersburg Central Pedagogic Institute in the science and mathematics faculty.

After a few years as a private tutor at St. Petersburg University, he was granted permission by the Russian Minister of Public Instruction to study abroad. Mendeleev broadened his theoretical and experimental background by study with leading chemists at Paris and Heidelberg. On his return to Russia, he was appointed professor of chemistry in the Technological Institute. He became professor of chemistry at St. Petersburg in 1866.

Mendeleev can best be described as a practical chemist rather than a theoretician and one whose first interest was in education. His *Principles of Chemistry* was a textbook. It contained his periodic table, which was and still is an excellent way of introducing students to the study of chemical elements. The *Principles of Chemistry* was a remarkably successful book, which appeared in eight Russian editions, three English editions, and several in French and German.

In 1863 Mendeleev published an encyclopedia of chemical technology. He became the Russian government's expert on fuels and in that capacity conducted studies of the oil fields in the Caucasus. The government also sent him to the Pennsylvania oil fields. In 1889 he made an economic study of the Donetz coal basin. At the end of his career, the Russian government made him head of the Department of Weights and Measures.

Mendeleev's conception of the periodic table was that it was a natural, if not inevitable, result of the known facts. He told afterwards how "the law of periodicity was thus a direct outcome of the stock of generalisations and established facts which had accumulated by the end of the decade 1860-1870: it is an embodiment of those data in a more or less systematic expression." The data or information that became available was the correct atomic weights of the elements. Mendeleev recalled that little hope was held that the international meeting at Karlsruhe in 1860 would arrive at an agreement on these weights. He "vividly" remembered "the impression produced by his [Cannizzaro's] speeches, which admitted of no compromise, and seemed to advocate truth itself. . . ." The conflicting theories on atomic structure that had resulted in disagreement on atomic weights was finally cleared up, as far as Mendeleev was concerned, at Karlsruhe.

The idea that the atomic weights of elements were related by some simple mathematical rule occurred to several investigators during the 1860's. Mendeleev knew of seven men working towards a solution. Another factor that contributed to the discovery of the periodic table was the researches on the rare elements, like mobium and vanadium. It was found that they had properties that were strikingly similar to each other and to other elements.

All of these things together—more certainty as to atomic weights, the suggestion by some as to their relationship according to some "simple law," and the revealing of the similarity of the rare elements—had brought chemical investigators, Mendeleev believed, to the point where there was "but one step to the discovery of the law of periodicity." Of course he said this after his discovery and who can judge how many steps the unsuccessful efforts of dozens of other men were from discovery. "Nevertheless, the fruit was ripening," and Mendeleev later found that several chemists were close but "they merely wanted the boldness necessary to place the whole question at such a height that its reflection on the facts could be clearly seen."[8]

The originality of Mendeleev's approach lay in his comparison of the difference in atomic weights with what he called *pendulum-oscillations.* The key to a geometrical analysis, which he considered the basis of all exact science, was in Dalton's law of multiple proportions. The law stated that compounds were formed by an atom-to-atom link. Since compounds must consist of some whole number of atoms, the weight of a molecule of a compound will differ from another by some multiple of the weights of the constituent atoms. Mendeleev reasoned that atomic weights increased in a similar multiple or step-wise manner. Earlier attempts were based on grouping the elements in triads or octaves. Others worked on the idea of continuity and arranged the elements on curves. One chemist used a spiral construction and another a telluric helix. Mendeleev arranged the elements in a table which fit what he believed was the natural step-wise order.

The idea of the periodic table of elements was explained in Mendeleev's *Principles of Chemistry,* first published in 1869, and in the same year he described the table to the Russian Chemical Society. The elements, he said, if arranged according to their atomic weights, exhibited a periodicity of properties. Elements with similar chemical properties have nearly the same atomic weights (e.g., platinum, iridium, osmium) or if not the same weights, the weights of similar elements can be found, by multiplying the lighter elements by some whole number. This arrangement in groups by atomic weight corresponded to the valency of the elements. The table showed that the magnitude of the atomic weight determined the character of the element just as the magnitude of the molecule determined the character of a compound. The elements that are most widely diffused have small atomic weights.

Mendeleev drew eight conclusions from an interpretation of the periodic table. The first five statements, mentioned above, contain nothing startling. This information was undeniably useful in teaching, but it was not of exceptional theoretical importance. But then Mendeleev added that "we must expect the discovery of many yet *unknown* elements" and he followed up this prediction by claiming that the table could be used for determining atomic weights more accurately. Finally, he stated that the periodic table could foretell properties of elements from their atomic weights.[9]

Mendeleev's use of the periodic table to predict the existence of unknown elements was dramatic. There was something awesome in the way he confidently said that there were three undiscovered elements, which he called eka-aluminum, eka-boron, and eka-silicon. He then proceeded to describe the properties, such as atomic weight, specific gravity, solubility, of the as yet undiscovered elements. Mendeleev became a well-known name and the periodic table a subject of special interest when the three elements, as described, were discovered: gallium (1874), scandium (1879), and germanium (1885).

Like Cannizzaro, Mendeleev had not discovered new facts. Both organized known facts to prove a point and, interestingly, both used the results primarily as a teaching aid. There is no question that the periodic table was an original contribution to science. Some may doubt that it deserves to be classed alongside Maxwell's electromagnetic theory of light. Mendeleev sought a method of arranging chemical elements in some mathematical order and, in so doing, found that the periodic table was useful as a guide into an unknown territory of nature. Yet Maxwell's theory is considered more important than Mendeleev's, and the basis for comparison is the vastness of the territory opened. There is no acceptable criteria for evaluating a theory by judging the degree of originality required or by estimating the difficulty in making it.

Mendeleev's construction of the periodic table illustrates what Ernst Mach called "the principle of comparison in physics." A theory, Mach believed, was a combination of memory and comparison. He was speaking in 1894. Facts were organized by a theory to make them easier to remember, but theory also placed them alongside previously discovered facts, or "a well-known physiognomy." He went so far as to say that "theory differs from observation neither in the mode of its origin nor in its last results." Both theory and observation were means of increasing the number of facts. Mach's philosophy of science would place a high value on the theory of the periodic table and, at the same time, reduce the importance of the law of conservation of energy. The main object of science was to extend knowledge, Mach thought. "It is this *rapidity* in extending knowledge," he said, "that gives to theory a preference over simple observation."[10]

Electric Force

6   The British Association for the Advancement of
Science "Report on the Recent Progress and Present Condition of
the Mathematical Theories of Electricity, Magnetism, and Heat,"
published in 1835, suggested that the sciences of electricity,
magnetism, and heat be treated together. The three, electricity,
magnetism, and heat, were to be treated analogously because
they had "sufficient connexion, both in mathematical reasoning
by which they have been established and the philosophical
principles on which they depend. . . ."

The *Report* went on to discuss the assumption of one or two
fluids as being the "true cause" of electrical phenomena. That a
fluid was the cause was "proved by the facts" and especially the
mechanical effects such as shock, power of striking, breaking, and
penetrating. The *Report's* conclusions were that electrical, magnetic, and heat theory could be developed by analogy with each
other and that the "physical truth" behind electrical phenomena
was explained by the two fluid theory.[1]

William R. Grove, inventor of the battery which was named
after him and who was a part-time physicist, was one of the first
to doubt the fluid theory of electricity. In a paper published in

1842, Grove said that he had considered "all the known classes of electrical phenomena" and he discovered that electrical effects were known "to us only as changes of ordinary matter." It seemed to him "as easy to imagine these changes to be effected by a force acting in definite directions, as by a fluid. . . ." He concluded that "as the idea of the hypothetical fluid is pursued, it gradually vanishes, and resolves itself into the idea of force."[2]

The question of whether electricity consisted of a fluid or a force was complicated further by the controversy as to whether electrical action could be exerted at a distance or whether it required an intervening medium. It seemed reasonable that electricity should outgrow the concept of an imponderable "fluid" because the discovery of so many different phenomena made the idea of an imponderable awkward and finally untenable. In this metamorphosis, electrical theory resembled the evolution of chemical theory, which had to abandon the imponderable phlogiston, and heat theory, which was forced to give up the idea of an imponderable caloric.

But why should the controversy between action-at-a-distance and an intervening medium continue? A similar question had been raised when Newton proposed his universal law of gravitation. What made electricity different from gravity was its many-sidedness. Gravity involved attraction only, but in electricity there was attraction, repulsion, induction, and chemical electrolysis. So many different phenomena, so many different ways of looking at electricity and magnetism challenged the imagination. When a scientist chose sides in the action-at-a-distance versus medium controversy, he automatically elected the analogy he would use in dealing with electricity. The dividing line in the controversy followed national boundaries. The French chose action-at-a-distance.

Around 1785 a Frenchman, Charles-Augustin Coulomb, succeeded in showing experimentally that Newton's inverse square law for gravity also applied to statically charged bodies. In addition, he used geometry to develop some more general ideas about the distribution of electric charge on spheres. Poisson, another French mathematician, found general solutions to the questions of electric charges on any shaped body and Poisson's work corroborated the results of Coulomb's experiments. Finally,

Ampère's work in electrodynamics included the idea of action-at-a-distance.

Mathematicians, like physicists or chemists, seek the widest possible generality for their work. The ultimate in generality for a mathematician is an equation with no physical limitations. For example, Laplace's and Fourier's equations have achieved the status of mathematical truths and they can also be applied to various physical problems. Each began with a physical problem, Laplace with gravity and Fourier with heat. Their solutions were so general that by analogy their mathematics could be applied to phenomena seemingly unrelated to their original concerns.

For their own purposes, mathematicians kept a physical image of the phenomena, but with the objective of widest possible generality in mind, they shied away from marrying their work to a physical hypothesis. Coulomb's attitude was typical of this type of caution. "I warn the reader," he wrote in 1788, "in order to put the following theory out of the reach of all systematic dispute, that in the supposition of two electric fluids I have no other intention than to present the results of calculation and of experiment with the smallest possible number of elements, and," he emphasized an unwillingness to be limited, "not to indicate the true cause of electricity."[3]

How influential mathematical theory can be in developing physical theory is demonstrated by a paper, privately published in 1828, titled "An Essay on the Application of Mathematical Analysis to the Theories of Electricity and Magnetism." The life of its author, George Green, was as obscure as the paper was well-known.

George Green was born in 1793 near Nottingham, England. His father was a miller, the *Dictionary of National Biography* says, "with private means." Very little is known of his early education except that he was almost entirely self-taught in mathematics and as a very young child showed "great talent for figures." The "Essay on the Application of Mathematical Analysis. . ." was Green's first and most important work. It was published at the relatively advanced age, for a mathematician, of thirty-five and was followed by only nine other papers, bringing Green's lifetime output of papers to ten.

At the age of forty, Green entered Cambridge University as a freshman. He did very well at Cambridge and was head of the freshman mathematical list. He took his degree in 1837 as fourth wrangler in the mathematical tripos. That he did not do better is not surprising, as his biographer wrote in the *Dictionary of National Biography*: "Green's want of familiarity with ordinary boys' mathematics prevented him from coming to the top in a time race."

Recognition came almost too late for Green. He was elected a Fellow of Caius College in 1839 but he died soon afterward, in 1841, at forty-seven.

Green's lack of formal education undoubtedly accounted for his extraordinarily original work. He was drawn to the study of electricity, he wrote, because of the challenge of submitting such a "power of universal agency" to calculation. Green acknowledged being influenced by Laplace, Poisson, and Fourier. In the introduction to his "Essay," Green remarked on the "extraordinary powers" of mathematics as an instrument of analysis for the physical sciences. He used Fourier's work in heat as an example of the effectiveness of mathematics. A "cursory view" of all that had been written on the mathematical theory of electricity convinced Green that the work published up until then, 1828, was "adapted only to particular objects, and that some general method, capable of being employed in every case, is still wanting."[4]

Some ideas are like fuses. Their ability to stimulate other men's thoughts magnifies their importance. One man was so affected by Green's "Essay" that he succeeded in making the ideas expressed there of singular importance to the history of nineteenth century science. Green's proponent was William Thomson, who in turn strongly influenced James Clerk Maxwell's intellectual evolution in electrical theory. Maxwell and Thomson, the Great Scots of nineteenth century science, in their divergent careers exemplify the exceptional aspects of British science, which was so original and creative.

William Thomson was born of Scottish parents in 1824 in Belfast. Maxwell was seven years his junior and was born in Edinburgh. Both men were left motherless at early ages and their schooling was carefully supervised by their fathers. Thomson's father was professor of mathematics at the University of

Glasgow and he taught his son himself rather than send him to grammar school. Thomson entered the University of Glasgow at ten and Maxwell went to Edinburgh University when he was sixteen.

Both men completed their formal education at Cambridge. Thomson entered when he was seventeen and took his degree after four years. He came out second wrangler in the mathematical tripos and was first in the Smith's Prize competition. While at Cambridge, Thomson was a student of William Hopkins, the most effective mathematical coach at Cambridge at that time.

Maxwell went to Cambridge in 1850 when he was nineteen and took his degree in 1854. His record at the university was almost a duplicate of Thomson's. Maxwell was second wrangler in the mathematical tripos and he too was first Smith's prizeman. William Hopkins was also Maxwell's mathematical tutor.

Thomson succeeded to the chair of natural philosophy at the University of Glasgow when he was twenty-two and he remained there for fifty-three years, retiring in 1899. Maxwell's academic career was more erratic. He held a chair of natural philosophy at Marischal College in Aberdeen, but lost it when the college was consolidated three years later. He then became professor of natural philosophy at King's College, London, which position he held for five years when he retired to his estate and private life. In 1871 Maxwell was induced to accept the first chair in experimental physics at Cambridge. He became the first head of the Cavendish Laboratory at Cambridge in 1874. To Thomson goes the priority for having established at Glasgow the first university physics laboratory in Great Britain. This was in 1846.

Both Thomson and Maxwell were generalists. Maxwell who was a *scientific* generalist did work ranging from geometrical construction to electrical theory and included competent work on such topics as the color composition of light and the nature of Saturn's rings. Besides his university lecturing, he found the time to lecture to workingmen on general topics of science and to write several lucid articles for the *Encyclopedia Brittannica*. Maxwell's major contribution was to electromagnetic theory and he made a first rank contribution to the kinetic theory of gases.

Maxwell had a variety of interests and activities, but they all centered within the scientific enterprise. He was a man who saw similarities and analogies in nature where others could only see differences. He was a man whose ideas crisscrossed lines of specialization, finding inspiration in one place to be applied to a problem in another.

There is a difference between an active intellect that ranges widely within a discipline like science and a more gregarious type that does not seem willing to be so confined. Thomson's interest was fully as much outside of science as it was inside. His work in engineering, for example, in the Atlantic cable, was part of a continuing interest in the application of science. Within the confines of the scientific field, Thomson worked in such seemingly diverse fields as thermodynamics and electricity.

The two men were generalists: one, remaining within the limits of scientific research, produced ideas of more profundity; the other, more restless, was more stimulating than profound. Thomson diffused scientific knowledge within and without the scientific community, and Maxwell, stimulated by Thomson who was his mentor, contributed to scientific theory.

Early in 1854, Maxwell, who had just received his degree from Cambridge, wrote to Thomson asking advice on what to read "so as to get a little insight" into the subject of electricity. Thomson, in a long letter, laid out a program of study and by November, 1854, Maxwell reported that he had involved himself in every branch of the subject simultaneously. He wrote that "the whole mass of confusion [was] beginning to clear up under the influence of a few simple ideas." The idea of electricity of tension was made easier because, he said, "I was greatly aided by the analogy of the conduction of heat, which I believe is your invention. . . ." Maxwell was to continue along the line of development begun by Thomson and the younger man readily admitted that he had "got a good deal out of you on electrical subjects, both directly & through the printer & publisher. . . ."[5]

The publications Maxwell referred to had been written in 1842 and 1847. The first paper, "On Uniform Motion of Heat in Homogeneous Solid Bodies, and Its Connexion with the Mathematical Theory of Electricity," was published anonymously by the seventeen-year-old Thomson. The second paper, first published in France, was on "The Elementary Laws of Statical Electricity." Thomson took Coulomb's laws as postulates and then, as he said, "by a very simple analysis first given by Green, we arrive at the laws of Faraday as theorems."

In 1844 Thomson had written in his diary that he had "long been entertaining a project of writing a series of essays on the mathl. theory of electricity, commencing with the fundamental principles, and giving all the applications of the general theorems relative to attraction, which are of use in giving a comprehensive view of the subject." He did not have a definite plan at that date and reluctantly put the project aside until after he took his degree.[6] The first paper, which was published in 1842, had only opened the subject for him. Soon after his graduation in 1845, he finished the second paper and the two papers constituted, Thomson claimed, a full theory of Faraday's lines of force. The two papers completed "the analogy with the theory of the conduction of heat. . . ."[7]

Another analogy for dealing with electricity occurred to Thomson while he was preparing his introductory lecture of his first course at Glasgow. (No wonder Thomson's lectures often seemed disjointed to his students. When original ideas like this occurred to him he talked about them aloud and to the students they seemed, and were, off the assigned topic.) The idea was that magnetism and electricity could be represented by an elastic solid under strain. His first analogy had been a result of combining Fourier's theory on heat with Green's concept of electric potential. This second analogy Thomson referred to as being a "mechanico-cinematical" representation of electric and magnetic forces. The article appeared in 1847 and was titled "On a Mechanical Representation of Electric, Magnetic, and Galvanic Forces." In the article Thomson wrote that the idea for this approach to the study of electricity had been suggested to him by Faraday's *Experimental Researches in Electricity*. The question, which had posed itself and which Thomson had solved in this article, was: might there be a problem in the theory of elastic solids "corresponding to every problem connected with the distribution of electricity on conductors, or with forces of attraction and repulsion exercised by electrified bodies."[8]

These articles represented the extent of Thomson's penetration of problems in electrical theory. He was an originator of ideas and of too restless an intellectual nature to pursue the suggestions to any great depth. In 1847 Thomson was involved in the problems of a newly appointed professor. During the summer he worked on several papers, one of which was given at the fall meeting of the British Association for the Advancement of Science. It was probably this meeting more than anything else that diverted Thomson from the study of electricity for the time being. At the British Association meeting of 1847, Thomson heard Joule's paper on the convertibility of electricity, heat, and mechanical motion. The discussion there and afterwards with Joule started Thomson on a long series of researches on heat which resulted in his absolute temperature scale and his independent discovery of the second law of thermodynamics. For the next six or eight years, Thomson's free time (while not teaching) was devoted to the study of heat, part of it in collaboration with Joule.

There were never projects wanting and Thomson was never without the urge to try something new. His interest was not limited to science. He once told the Institution of Civil Engineers that there was no "greater mistake than that of looking superciliously upon practical applications of science." Many of the greatest advances in physical science, Thomson said, "have been made in the earnest desire to turn the knowledge of the properties of matter to some purpose useful to mankind." He compared the advances of science with that of mathematics which "have been made through the desire of discovering the solution of problems which were of a highly practical kind in mathematical science. . . ." He left no doubt as to his opinion: "The life and soul of science is its practical application. . . ."[9]

Thomson was elected to the board of directors of the Atlantic Telegraph Company in 1856. The company immediately undertook to lay a submarine cable and Thomson was actively involved in the project, even going along with several of the expeditions that attempted the feat. The cable was finally successfully completed in 1866; in large part the success was due to Thomson's invention of a hypersensitive telegraph receiver.

It is apparent from the variety of scientific and engineering projects Thomson was involved in that he could barely have time to follow up on his very suggestive work in electrical theory. While Maxwell was doing his work in the 1850's and 1860's, Thomson was occupied with thermodynamics and submarine telegraph, in addition to many other less important efforts. What is just as apparent from some study of Thomson's life is that he was not interested in pursuing work in electrical theory any further. His was the type of intellect that probed but did not seek to penetrate.

Maxwell's interest in the world was almost as fully universal as Thomson's. There were differences that account for the diversity in their approach to electrical theory. Where Fourier's ideas on the motion of heat dominated Thomson's thinking all of his life, mechanics, or more especially dynamics, was Maxwell's central intellectual theme. His outlook was due considerably to his father's influence. Maxwell's father spent considerable time with the boy inspecting manufacturing works and looking at structures. When Maxwell sought a vacation from his preparation for the tripos at Cambridge, he decided to visit a friend at Birmingham. Such an opportunity should not be lost, his father wrote him, to "view, if you can, armourers, gunmaking and gunproving—swordmaking and proving—*Papier-mâché* and japanning—silver-plating by cementation and rolling—ditto, electrotype. . . ." The list would have appeared endless to some other son but apparently not to James. His father ended the letter with instructions, which if followed, left the son no time for rest. "If you have had enough of the town lots of Birmingham," the father wrote, "you could vary the recreation by viewing Kenilworth, Warwick, Leamington, Stratford-on-Avon, or such like."[10]

His father's insistence on the importance of manufacturing could have just as likely resulted in Maxwell becoming an engineer had not Maxwell's bent been more theoretical and more mathematical than required for engineering.

Maxwell could and did concentrate on more than one subject at a time. In the letters written to Thomson, primarily on electrical subjects, can be found mention of his various interests at the time. "I do not know what special subject you are busy with now," Maxwell wrote in 1856. "My special study is Elementary Mechanics and just at present parabolic motion." The next day he wrote to Thomson: "Here is my present notion about plasticity of homogeneous amorphous solids."[11] There was in every one of his letters to Thomson some mention of new ideas in several different fields while at the same time he discussed his advancements in electrical theory.

Maxwell began his study of electricity and magnetism with certain preconceptions. All investigators have preconceptions, but Maxwell was more conscious of having them than were most. He later wrote that at the outset of his investigation he "resolved to read no mathematics on the subject till I had first read through Faraday's *Experimental Researches in Electricity.* I was aware that there was supposed to be a difference between Faraday's way of conceiving phenomena and that of mathematicians, so that neither he nor they were satisfied with each other's language." According to Maxwell's understanding of the matter, "this discrepancy did not arise from either party being wrong."[12]

Faraday apparently believed that difficulty in "language" lay at the bottom of the controversy. He wrote to Maxwell in 1857 asking whether mathematicians could not put their conclusions "in common language as fully, clearly, and definitely as in mathematical formulae? If so, would it not be a great boon to such as I. . . ."[13]

But "language" is not the word to portray the differences in imagery or in method of working with ideas in electricity or magnetism. The difference between Faraday's method and the mathematicians' was that Faraday insisted upon the necessity of a medium and the mathematicians easily made use of action-at-a-distance. It was more than a matter of translating from one language into another. Faraday, the experimentalist with no competence in mathematics, had developed his own imagery based on the idea of lines of force. The mathematicians, such as Ampère, Gauss, and Weber, represented the exertion of magnetic and electromagnetic force by formula. Their conception was action between points and there was precedence for this approach in Newton.

Was there a relationship between phenomena being studied by Faraday and the mathematicians? There seemed to be, as attested by the experimental results of Oersted and Faraday. If everyone was talking about related phenomena, did the differences then stem from one being wrong and the other right, or was it as Maxwell·said, merely a difference of conceptualization? Since the two groups were looking at electromagnetic phenomena from such different vantage points, it would require more than translation to bring them into agreement. The problem was like the difference between an artist's conception of a nude and the same figure as seen by means of an X-ray machine. Maxwell had really undertaken a much bigger job than he thought, but he could not know how deep the roots were until he started to dig.

Some eminent German scientists, such as Clausius, Gauss, and Weber, had in their minds, Maxwell believed, "some prejudice, or *a priori* objection, against the hypothesis of a medium in which the phenomena of radiation of light and heat and the electric actions at a distance take place." Maxwell aligned himself with the British faction and as testimony we have his words: "Now we are unable to conceive of propagation in time, except . . . as the propogation of a condition of motion or stress in a medium already existing in space. . . ."[14]

The success that the action-at-a-distance group had achieved in the application of mathematics had given additional weight to their theoretical speculations. Since, Maxwell feared, "students of electricity, turn to them [the German scientists] as the greatest authorities in mathematical electricity, would probably imbibe, along with their mathematical methods, their physical hypotheses.

"These physical hypotheses, however, are entirely alien from the way of looking at things which I adopt, and one object which I have in view is that some of those who wish to study electricity may. . . come to see that there is another way of treating the subject. . . ."[15]

Maxwell wrote to Thomson in September, 1855, that he had "been planning and partly executing a system of propositions about lines of force &c which may be *afterwards* applied to Electricity, Heat or Magnetism or Galvanism. . . ." He was mining ideas from many sectors, including Thomson's idea on electrical images, Faraday's electrotonic state, and Green's idea of potential. He was not only trying to find a correlation between these theories but he also sought a correlation between the phenomena they sought to explain. "One thing at least it [his method of combining ideas] suceeds in," Maxwell wrote, "it reduces to one principle not only the attraction of currents & the induction of currents but also the attraction of electrified bodies without any new assumption."

Was Thomson surprised, annoyed, or chagrined when he read in Maxwell's letter that Maxwell planned on putting all of these ideas into a paper if, that is, Thomson did not already have "the whole draught of the thing lying in loose papers and neglected only till you have worked out Heat or got a little spare time?"

Perhaps Thomson was amused by the deference shown by the younger man or by Maxwell's naiveté. Maxwell underestimated the amount of originality he was exercising. He was certain that Thomson had "the mathematical part of the theory in your desk all that you have to do is explain your results. . . ." And then Maxwell outlined the source of his ideas with the presumption that Thomson had arrived at the same conclusion: ". . . you are acquainted with Faraday's theory of lines of force & with Ampère's laws of currents and of course you must have wished at least to understand Ampère in Faraday's sense. You had the advantage of being well acquainted with V and with Green's essay. . . ."[16]

The results of Maxwell's first efforts were read on December, 1855, and February, 1856 before the Cambridge Philosophical Society. He titled the paper "On Faraday's Lines of Force." He introduced his subject by citing the "peculiarly unfavourable" state of electrical science. He cited the inadequacies of the existing theories as being wanting in proof or failing to show a relationship with the "other parts of the science. No electrical theory can now be put forth, unless it shews the connexion not only between electricity at rest and current electricity, but between the attractions and inductive effects of electricity in both states."

But someone making an attempt to develop such a unifying theory found it necessary to become "familiar with a considerable body of most intricate mathematics. . . ." The first step must be simplification so that the material will be in a form "in which the mind can grasp them." Maxwell saw two alternatives for the process of simplification. It could be in the form of mathematical formula, but "we entirely lose sight of the phenomena to be explained. . . ." This approach would also limit progress because "we can never obtain more extended views of the connexions of the subject." The other possibility was the adoption of a physical hypothesis whereby "we see the phenomena only through a medium, and we are liable to that blindness to facts and rashness in assumption which a partial explanation encourages." How to reason by use of physical ideas without adopting a physical hypothesis? The answer was physical analogy, which Maxwell defined as "that partial similarity between the laws of one science and those of another which makes each of them illustrate the other." The type of analogy he proposed to use was between heat and electrical attraction, and the credit for this approach he readily ascribed to William Thomson. The use of this kind of analogy was a means of presenting mathematical ideas for the study of electrical phenomena.[17]

Maxwell's predilection for mechanical and dynamical analogy becomes immediately evident. He invented a geometrical model of Faraday's lines of force. The model consisted of tubes corresponding to lines of force. The tubes were filled with an imponderable, incompressible fluid. He was careful to point out that he was not producing a physical hypothesis. The fluid that he had created was "not even a hypothetical fluid which is introduced to explain actual phenomena." This imaginary fluid, flowing in imaginary pipes, was merely a way of "establishing certain theorems in pure mathematics in a way more intelligible to many minds and more applicable to physical problems than that in which algebraic symbols alone are used." The equations for the conduction of heat were used in solving the problem of the flow of the imaginary fluid.

Maxwell hoped that his geometrical model would help produce a "mature theory, in which physical facts will be physically explained. . . ." Yet he had to confess that there existed "a professedly physical theory of electrodynamics, which is so elegant, so mathematical, and so entirely different from anything in this paper, that I must state its axioms. . . ." The theory he described was Wilhelm Weber's. Why then imagine an electrotonic state of Faraday's of which there was no physical conception? Maxwell answered that it was a good thing to have two ways of looking at electrical phenomena and "to admit that there *are* two ways. . . ." Besides, one had to accept the concept of action-at-a-distance in order to agree with Weber's theory.

Maxwell's approach to the study of electricity was clearly discernible in this first paper, "On Faraday's Lines of Force." He had, one might say *a priori,* rejected the idea of action-at-a-distance, which had been presented in such a mathematically elegant fashion by Weber. Maxwell required a physical concept. Faraday's idea of an electrotonic state was really a chemist's viewpoint, and Maxwell confessed that the idea had "not yet presented itself to my mind in such a form that its nature and properties may be clearly explained without reference to mere symbols. . . ."[18]

Thomson's analogy was suggestive to Maxwell, but it did not seem to touch his imagination either. Maxwell's recourse to a "hypothetical fluid" in motion showed that what appealed to his mind was an analogy, like Thomson's, but one which used the laws of mechanics and one which was dynamical. Matter in motion was the key Maxwell sought. This paper obviously would not satisfy his own criteria for a successful theory.

Maxwell did not return to electrical theory for five years. Either he did not feel ready to take the step he urged in the first paper or he was too busy with other work. He entered and won the Adams Prize Essay contest on the composition of Saturn's rings in 1856; he wrote a paper on the dynamical theory of gases in 1859 (this was his first contribution to the kinetic theory of gases). Each of these papers was an application of Maxwell's dynamical approach to matter and force. The stability of Saturn's rings was due to the equilibrium of particles in motion. The kinetic theory of gases showed that a presumably static effect, gas pressure, was the result of the motion of gas particles. So even though he may not have had time to think about electrical problems during these five years, Maxwell was expanding his concept of matter in motion.

Near the end of 1861, Maxwell wrote Thomson that he had "been trying to develope the dynamical theory of magnetism" after views stated by Thomson in 1856 and 1857. The magnetic medium, Maxwell supposed, was divided into cells and the cell walls consisted of spherical particles which were "electricity."[19] The idea of a medium was elaborated in this paper, "On

Physical Lines of Force," published in the *Philosophical Magazine* during 1861 and 1862.

For those, like himself, who could not conceive of a force produced between magnetic poles without a medium, Maxwell proposed to "clear the way for speculation in this direction." His object was to suggest a way that this medium could be made to produce all the known electrical and magnetic effects. He would use an analogy with mechanics and "by investigating the mechanical results of certain states of tension and motion in a medium, and comparing these with the observed phenomena of magnetism and electricity," he hoped to show that the idea of a medium was a plausible hypothesis. He had used geometrical concepts in the paper "On Faraday's Lines of Force," but he proposed now, Maxwell wrote, "to examine magnetic phenomena from a mechanical point of view." If the same approach would apply to electromagnetic phenomena and to those of induced currents, "we shall have found a theory which, if not true, can only be proved to be erroneous by experiments which will greatly enlarge our knowledge of this part of physics."[20]

Maxwell had to make some physical assumptions about the medium in order to deal with it in the mathematics of mechanics. In other words, he had to construct a model before he could interpret the action of the medium from a mechanical point of view. He invented the idea of eddies or vortices. The magnetic medium was divided into cylindrical-like shapes and these cylinders rotated about lines in space that were parallel to the lines of force.

A model, in Maxwell's conception, was not real; that is, it did not exist "in nature," and he was not even willing to assent to it as an electrical hypothesis. The model was, "however, a mode of connexion which is mechanically conceivable, and easily investigated, and it serves to bring out the actual mechanical connexions between the known electro-magnetic phenomena." The model was not an imitation of reality, but Maxwell ventured "to say that anyone who understands the provisional and temporary character of this hypothesis, will find himself rather helped than hindered by it in his search for the true interpretation of the phenomena."[21]

The success of Maxwell's model lay not only in unifying

mathematically and conceptually all electrical and magnetic phenomena but, in addition, the model worked so well that Maxwell was able to make discoveries by imagining its operation. The originality of the model came from his decision to use mechanics as the source of parts. When he found it difficult to get adjacent vortices to rotate in the same direction he hit upon the idea of using idle wheels, which were found in a typical gear train in power-driven machinery. He also remembered that idle wheels were capable of motion in some mechanisms, as for example, in the Siemens' governor for steam engines.

How ingenious, both electrically and mechanically! Mechanically, the dual operation of the vortices and the idle wheels between them illustrated the attraction and repulsions of magnets and currents. Electrically, the joint action between the vortices (magnetic lines of force) and idle wheels (electric currents) made it possible to imagine the connection between electricity and magnetism. Maxwell, in deducing the characteristics of the medium to account for phenomena, had to compute the medium's elasticity. He concluded that the "elasticity of the magnetic medium in air is the same as that of the luminiferous medium [the ether in the wave theory of light], if these two coexistent, coextensive, and equally elastic media are not rather one medium." There was further collaboration for this suggestion. "The velocity of transverse undulations in our hypothetical medium," Maxwell found to agree so exactly with that of the velocity of light "that we can scarcely avoid the inference that *light consists in the transverse undulations of the same medium which is the cause of electric and magnetic phenomena.*"[22]

There were differences between Ampère, Faraday, and Maxwell in the way they understood the phenomena and the way they developed their theories, but these differences were not as great as they or their proponents imagined. Ampère's was the strictly mathematical approach to nature. He worked out the relations between currents that were separated by space and that exerted forces on each other. The only assumption he made was that all magnetic effects were produced by currents of electricity. In this way he was typical of mathematicians, for example, Fourier, who only made assumptions in order to solve equations of too many variables. His first and major reliance was on mathematical deduction and he only made a physical assumption when stuck. He had simply taken as given the fact that wires did exert a force on each other across space.

Faraday could not imagine such an action and, being unschooled in mathematics, he could not follow mathematical methods of reasoning. He was a physicist or experimenter and he made his discoveries by physical conceptualization in conjunction with the use of his laboratory apparatus. Once the discovery was made, Faraday needed to explain it in his own mind, physically. He therefore invented the ideas of electrotonic state and lines of force.

Maxwell began as a mathematician and learned his physics by studying Faraday and Thomson. His own predilections and his teachers imbued him with the need for physical conceptualization. He could not accept Ampère's purely mathematical approach because he believed, with Faraday, that acceptance of Ampère required acceptance of the idea of action-at-a-distance. Maxwell, in the way he understood phenomena and the method of developing theories, fell somewhere between the mathematician, Ampère, and Faraday, the physicist. Maxwell was the first of the mathematical-physicists. His first venture into electrical theory, "On Faraday's Lines of Force," placed him closer to Faraday in his method of reasoning. The second paper, "On Physical Lines of Force," was more original and showed that Maxwell was moving in his own direction. The third paper, Maxwell's capstone, was creative and unique. In this paper, Maxwell not only made new discoveries but he demonstrated the fruitfulness of the new method, that of the mathematical-physicist.

There were two things that Maxwell insisted upon as necessary to this theory. One was that in order to produce electric and magnetic phenomena there must be a medium and that meant that he was concerned with what went on in "the space in the neighbourhood of the electric or magnetic bodies." The other tenet was that "in that space there is matter in motion, by which the observed electromagnetic phenomena are produced." His choice of a title, "A Dynamical Theory of the Electromagnetic Field," was a careful and significant selection of words.

Maxwell eschewed the model that was so helpful to him. In

speaking of "On Physical Lines of Force," he said that in the present paper "I avoid any hypotheses of this kind. . . ." He now used terms from a mechanical analogy merely as "illustrative, not as explanatory." Maxwell did describe the mode of reasoning that he preferred. In the place of Faraday's electrotonic state he used the term "electromagnetic momentum," which "depends on circumstances external to the conductor, then both induction of currents and electromagnetic attractions may be proved by mechanical reasoning."

Maxwell was unequivocal about his theory as to the dynamical nature of the electromagnetic field. Several times in the paper he made statements such as: "The energy in electromagnetic phenomena is mechanical energy. . . . On our theory it resides in the electromagnetic field, in the space surrounding the electrified and magnetic bodies. . . ." But his theory only represented his particular method of operation or approach, whereas "the conclusions arrived at in the present paper are independent of this hypothesis," he correctly claimed, "being deduced from experimental facts. . . ."[23]

Maxwell's theory as expressed in his equations gradually won acceptance. They succeeded in unifying all magnetic and electrical phenomena under a group of related equations. In addition, he had deduced from them the electromagnetic theory of light; that is, that electromagnetic phenomena and light phenomena were identical. Scientists did not, Maxwell insisted, need to accept the idea of the medium that he believed in so strongly. But the success of his mathematics gave very strong support to his way of thinking. Few scientists could follow his line of thought. Heinrich Hertz, who in 1887 experimentally demonstrated the electromagnetic theory of light, confessed that he could not understand Maxwell's approach but he did accept the equations. William Thomson, to whom Maxwell gave so much credit as the originator of his ideas, never seemed to grasp the theory. In 1888 Thomson referred to Maxwell's central idea as a "curious and ingenious, but not wholly tenable hypothesis."[24]

Maxwell's method, which was so successful in handling the most difficult question of the nineteenth century, was the result of an evolution in method or attitude of scientists. The experimentalist imagined an explanation in the form of unperceived phenomena to explain the results of their experiments. Maxwell reasoned by analogy, using models. The phenomena that he was trying to understand could be explained by models that operated *as if* they were capable of producing the observed results. On the one hand, Maxwell avoided the purely mathematical method, which was in danger of losing touch with reality. On the other hand, it was not necessary to create imponderables, which abridged the laws of nature in order to account for phenomena.

After Maxwell, the physical model, which was not a picture of reality but an aid to the imagination, became accepted. The nineteenth century had moved away from dependence on imaginary and unnatural imponderables that explained one phenomenon at a time, for this was the purpose of the imponderable. What had evolved was the mathematical abstraction that could encompass a great number of phenomena at once showing their relationship. The imagination stopped short of absolute abstraction and relied on a model which was a fictitious agency obeying natural laws. The idea that the cause of the phenomena was not only unimaginable but that it was unnecessary to try to imagine the cause was to be a feature of twentieth century science. Whether the twentieth century is the ultimate or not of abstraction, one thing that can be seen is that twentieth century abstraction is a direct outcome of Maxwell's method.

Light Waves

7   When an old controversy was renewed at the beginning of the nineteenth century, it had the same drama of the earlier one and again scientists were divided over the same question. The question was whether light was matter (particles) or form, which meant motion of a medium.

The first man to challenge the view accepted by the eighteenth century failed to win support for his theory. Another man succeeded in establishing the new principle a little over a decade later. We have in the history of light in the nineteenth century not only the drama of controversy but the puzzle of what constitutes the ingredients of success for a theory. The history illustrates the dual relationship between the origins of a theory and its acceptance. In one sense the origin of a theory, who proposed it and why, determines its success. In another sense the origin itself, the impetus to put forward a new theory, is determined by a scientist's idea of what is acceptable.

It is possible to treat the development of scientific theories as the result of changing relationships between origins of a theory and its acceptance, if we conceive of science as invention rather than discovery. To think of science as discovery means to be able to accept only certain established methods of arriving at truth. When conceived as invention, science can be seen as a more imaginative enterprise with the scientist free to explore any avenue in order to understand new experience.[1] The history of science therefore must also consider the question of how man's untrammeled imagination is channeled into paths that lead to acceptable theories.

A letter with the title "Outlines of Experiments and Inquiries respecting Sound and Light" was read to the Royal Society on January 16, 1800. The letter was from Thomas Young, M.D., F.R.S., and was dated July 8, 1799, at Emmanuel College, Cambridge. Young wrote that he had wanted for some time to transmit the results of experiments that he had performed on the subject of sound but had delayed in order to have collected more data. But in that summer of 1799 he began to feel that the magnitude of the investigation might "occupy the leisure hours of some years, or perhaps of a life," so he determined to submit some conclusions already formed.[2] In the midst of a long and detailed discussion of his experiments on sound, Young interjected heading "X. Of the Analogy between Light and Sound." In that section he discussed his proposition that the wave theory of light received strong support from an analogy between the colors produced by light passing through thin glass plates and the sounds of a series of organ pipes. And, he added, this analogy gave a more satisfactory explanation of the phenomena than occurred in Newton's particle theory.[3]

The man who reopened the wave-theory-versus-particle-theory-of-light controversy was a physicist by avocation. Thomas Young was born in 1773. His parents were both members of the Society of Friends. Not too much can be made of the fact that he was the member of a dissenting sect because in most ways he led a traditional life. In addition, Young was successfully opposed in his views on the wave theory by a member of another dissenting sect. Young's father owned considerable property, and money never seems to have been a problem in Thomas Young's life.

An exceptional youth, Young could read at two years of age

and was studying Latin, Greek, and mathematics when he was nine. By fourteen he had also studied Hebrew, Chaldee, Syriac, and Persian, and at that age was serving as a tutor in the classics. Young was introduced by an uncle to most of the distinguished literary men of London and was recognized by them as a classical scholar "of no mean order." He was then eighteen.

Young chose medicine as a profession. He studied medicine at St. Bartholomew's Hospital, Edinburgh, and was made a doctor of "physic" at Göttingen in 1796. He received an M.D. from Cambridge in 1808. In 1799 Young began practice as a physician in London and was elected physician at St. George's Hospital, London, in 1811. He retained that position for the rest of his life. In 1814 Young retired from medical practice and was appointed "inspector of calculations" to the Palladium Insurance Company. He made important contributions to medical literature, writing on the mechanism of the eye, the circulation of the blood, and consumptive diseases. He often found his medical responsibilities in danger of neglect because of his other activities, and it was in these "other activities" that he obtained recognition.

Young was elected a Fellow of the Royal Society in 1794 on the basis of a paper he read on the physiology of the eye. But he was not to have a career in science. He resigned a lecturership that he held at the Royal Institution after only two years. His friends believed that his work at the Institution interfered with his prospects as a physician. But it was also said that his lectures at the Institution were not a success because they were "too didactic and condensed" to be popular. Apparently, it was not his competency as a scientist that was at question; Young was simply not an effective lecturer. A course of lectures that he gave on medicine during 1808 and 1809 were "too condensed" and were only "sparsely attended."

A restless, imaginative, and well-disciplined intellect was Young's hallmark. He was expert in three languages and competent in ten, altogether. His interest in linguistics brought him in contact with the Rosetta stone, the key to Egyptian hieroglyphics. He discovered in 1815 that the hieroglyphics were not all alphabetic but that some were symbolic. The subject claimed part of his interest for the rest of his life, and he contributed not only the beginning of a hieroglyphic vocabulary but also many non-alphabetic signs. As an Egyptologist Young's reputation was well established through articles in journals and through his contributions to the *Encyclopedia Britannica.*

Medicine never seemed to absorb him and he was quoted as saying that he had acquired "a pretty good proportion of those things for which affluence is principally desired . . . but I am not the more in love with my profession." A contemporary believed that Young "was either not fitted for a physician, or was too engrossed in other pursuits" to have been successful.[4]

Young's interest in natural philosophy (physics) stemmed from his studies for the medical degree. He wrote that he had chosen the topic "Formation of the Human Voice" as a topic to fulfill part of the requirements for his degree in "physic" at Göttingen. When he began working on the essay of the voice, he found that he had very little conception of what sound was, and finding no references available, he began original research and experiments on sound. The close resemblance between the phenomena of sound and the color of thin plates, an optical phenomenon, led Young "to suspect the existence of a closer analogy between them that I could before have easily believed."[5]

The Royal Society invited Young to give the Bakerian Lecture in 1800. The title of the lecture was "On the Mechanism of the Eye." In it he determined the refractive power of a variable medium and applied the results to the crystalline lens of the eye. His medical studies had concentrated on the operation of the ear and eye. From these considerations he had moved in stages to the study of sound and light. The 1800 paper was a step away from physiology into the area of physical optics.

Young was invited again in 1801 to give the Bakerian Lecture. He was listed then as professor of natural philosophy of the Royal Institution, and the title of his talk, "On the Theory of Light and Colours." This time Young ventured into the particle-wave theory controversy, but he did so cautiously. "The object of the present dissertation is not so much to propose any opinions which are absolutely new," he said, "as to refer some theories, which have been already advanced, to their original inventors, to support them by additional evidence, and to apply them to a great number of diversified facts, which have hitherto been buried in obscurity."[6] The authority quoted by Young, strangely enough, was Newton. Long passages were given from Newton's writings, including Newton's rejection of the wave theory: "The waves, pulses, or vibrations of the air, wherein sounds consist, bend manifestly, though not so much as the waves of water. For a bell or a cannon may be heard beyond a hill which intercepts the sight of the sounding body; and sounds are propogated as readily through crooked pipes as straight ones. But light is never known to follow crooked passages nor to bend into the shadow." Therefore, Newton concluded, since it was accepted that sound consisted of wave motion and light did not exhibit the same characteristics, "Are not all hypotheses erroneous in which light is supposed to consist in pression or motion propagated through a fluid medium?"

The strategy in Young's approach is evident. Someone without reputation or status in a field, such as a medical man speaking on physics, needs "authority" to support his arguments. To Englishmen of the nineteenth century, Newton was still *the* authority on all questions of science. How unfortunate that the great Newton had carried his speculations so far that he appeared to be in conflict with the theory that Young was trying to establish. Young's use of Newton was more than a clever scheme, it was astute.

". . . The *Principia* does not directly contradict this proposition" that light consists of a wave motion in the ether, Young claimed. Newton had simply not taken into account the radical difference between the ether, which transmitted light, and the media, (air or water, for example), which transmitted sound. "On the whole. . .", Young concluded, the wave theory "may be safely admitted as perfectly consistent with analogy and with experiment."[7]

Young, like Newton, relied on analogy between sound and light. To explain the colors of scratches on a polished surface, Young noted that "there is a striking analogy between this separation of colours, and the production of a musical note by successive echoes from equidistant iron pallisades. . . ." Young's most important contribution to the development of the theory of light was the concept of interference, which supposed that waves of light could augment or cancel each other. If a crest of one wave meets a trough of another, "they will both be destroyed"; but when crest meets crest the result will be augmentation. The same principle of interference accounted for beats of sound caused by echoes, a phenomenon that Young described.

After a carefully developed presentation of his arguments in favor of the undulatory, or wave, theory of light, Young permitted himself some speculations. Light, he believed, was *analogous* to sound, but it appeared to be *identical* with heat. ". . . At present, it seems highly probable that light differs from heat only in the frequency of its undulations or vibrations; those undulations which are within certain limits, with respect to frequency, being capable of affecting the optic nerve and constituting light. . . ."

In his conclusion Young exhibited the assurance requisite for the presentation of a new idea. He had begun by citing Newton's authority but had concluded by proposing the adoption of a theory that Newton had rejected. If there were those who still doubted his theory of interference and the wave motion of light, Young believed it would be "easy to enter more minutely into the details of various experiments, and to show the insuperable difficulties attending the Newtonian doctrines. . . ." Young was not an iconoclast. The image of Newton was unmarred, he believed, by his dissent, which Young maintained was minor. Newton, Young said, had merits in natural philosophy which were "great beyond all contest or comparison; his optical discovery of the composition of white light, would alone have immortalised his name. . . ."[8]

Later, when under attack for having contradicted Newton, Young retorted: "Much as I venerate the name of Newton, I am not therefore obliged to believe that he was infallible. I see . . . with regret that he was liable to err, and that his authority has, perhaps, sometimes even retarded the progress of science."[9]

In 1803 Young was again asked to give the Royal Society's Bakerian Lecture, which he titled "Experiments and Calculations relative to Physical Optics." His assurance had obviously grown. This paper was short, only sixteen pages (his 1801 lecture, which was on light, was thirty-six pages). Gone in the 1803 lecture was the hesitancy that prompted him to quote so much of Newton in the previous talk. Young began in 1803 with a forthright statement: "The proposition on which I mean to insist at present is simply this—that fringes of colors are produced by the interference of two portions of light; and I think it will not be denied by the most prejudiced that the assertion is proved by the experiments I am about to relate. . . ."

The exposition naturally became clearer as a result of the development of Young's thinking on the matter. His statements no longer apologized for differing with Newton but declared that the proponents of Newton and the particle theory of light henceforth have the burden of proof on them. After describing experiments that supported his wave theory, Young said: "Those who are attached to the Newtonian theory of light . . . would do well to endeavour to imagine anything like an explanation of these experiments derived from their own doctrines; and if they fail in the attempt, to refrain at least from idle declamation against a system which is founded on the accuracy of its application to all these facts, and to a thousand others of a similar nature."[10]

From Scotland came the blast that undermined Young and according to some drove the wave theory out of Britain. The *Edinburgh Review,* which had just been founded in 1802, carried the following anonymous review of Young's Bakerian Lectures:

> As this paper contains nothing which deserves the name, either of experiment or discovery, and as it is in fact destitute of every species of merit, we should have allowed it to pass. . . . The dignities of the author, and the title of Bakerian Lecture, which is prefixed to these lucubrations, should not have saved them from a place in the ignoble crowd.

Not only was Young attacked but the diatribe was part of the growing criticism of the Royal Society, which gained momentum during the first decades of the nineteenth century. The writer continued:

But we have of late observed in the physical world a most unaccountable predilection for vague hypothesis daily gaining ground; and we are mortified to see that the Royal Society . . . is now, by the publication of such papers, giving the countenance of its highest authority to dangerous relaxations in the principles of physical logic.[11]

The review was written by Henry P. Brougham, who had a wide range of talents and interests, including writing, law, politics, education, and science. Brougham was educated at the University of Edinburgh, where he majored in humanities and philosophy but also "delighted" in the study of mathematics and physics. At the age of eighteen his paper, "Experiments and Observations on . . . Light," was accepted for publication by the Royal Society. He was lord chancellor and had a long career in the House of Commons, where he advocated legal reform and the abolition of slavery. His speech in support of the Reform Bill of 1831 was considered his masterpiece. It was full of sarcasm.

Brougham's interest in education prompted his inauguration of a series of mechanics institutes in the 1820's. In 1825 he published "Observations on the Education of the People," which passed through twenty editions before the end of that year. His idea for the publication of useful works at low cost resulted in the formation of the Society for the Diffusion of Useful Knowledge in 1825. The University of London was founded in 1828, through his efforts, to provide a scientific education for the upper classes.

The review of Young's work that Brougham wrote is not surprising. Brougham's main interest was not science and one can see he was not competent to judge the value of original work. It was said that all the reviews he wrote for the *Edinburgh Review* were "slashing," "often superficial," and "scandalously unjust."[12] This accounts for one unfavorable evaluation of Young's new theory. But opposition by one man, and a nonscientist at that, is never enough to ruin a theory's chances for success, especially when there is support by the scientific community. No such support was forthcoming in 1804. Why not?

Brougham had said that Young's work consisted of "vague

hypothesis," and by this expression it is assumed he meant it was insufficiently demonstrated by experiment. There is no rule for determining the sufficiency of evidence. The greater the predilection for the idea, the less evidence a scientist requires. Certainly Newton's particle theory of light was based on less experimental evidence than Young's theory. Take as another case Newton's suggestion of the existence of an ether, which was fantastic, yet accepted. He wrote of a substance that was 700,000 times more elastic than air and 700,000 times more rare. Would this idea not have been laughed at had it not borne the imperateur of the discoverer of the universal law of gravitation? Young suffered under the extreme disadvantage of not having a large enough reputation to support a new and controversial idea.

Another difficulty that hindered Young was what was called a style that was, "in general, far from clear" and, in addition, he lacked "mathematical training."[13] The attributes that Young lacked in order to be convincing to other scientists may have cost him the support of such people as William Hyde Wollaston. But Wollaston had also hesitated in accepting Dalton's atomic theory due, it appears, to the "want of that bold and enterprising spirit of speculation which is more or less essential to those who make great revolutions in science."[14] The irony of that statement is that Young himself was not one of those "bold and enterprising spirits," as can be seen by his carefully conservative manner of presentation of his ideas to the Royal Society.

It was not, after all, Brougham's opposition that "drove" the wave theory of light out of Britain. The difficulty was that Young had no support for his idea. Neither the Royal Society nor any member of it came forward in his defense. Brougham's biting criticism rankled Young, but when he came to make a reply he had no other avenue than a private publication of his own, which was not widely circulated. One can only guess why the Royal Society invited Young to give the Bakerian Lecture twice on the subject of the wave theory of light. The first lecture he gave was filled with references from Newton and was carefully phrased so that it may not have seemed controversial. True, the second lecture on light, "Experiments and Calculations relative to Physical Optics" (1803), did forthrightly support the wave theory. Young was not asked again.

Young had shown a proper amount of circumspection in presenting his new idea before the venerable Society. He was, he argued, only modifying a theory that had first been proposed by Christian Huygens in 1690 and the basis for that modification, Young claimed, could be found in Newton. Young's contribution was the idea of interference, or "beats." But as Brougham pointed out, Young's idea was highly controversial and in direct conflict with "authority," Newton. The Royal Society was not the place to present new ideas in the nineteenth century. It gave Young a hearing, but not the support of scientists, which he needed.

New ideas need new channels of expression. Soon after a new scientific society was formed, the British Association for the Advancement of Science, Young's wave theory of light received the kind of strong support that guaranteed acceptance, although not needed by that time.

In 1834 the British Association's "Report on the Progress and the Present State of Physical Optics" spoke of the wave theory as having undeniable "claims to our assent." "These claims are grounded on the vast body of new phenomena which it explains —and explains, (it is to be remembered,) not in a vague and general manner, but in the precise language of analysis, and with an accuracy which the refinements of modern observation have not been able to impugn." The *Report* concluded: "It may be confidently said that it possesses characters which no *false* theory ever possessed before."[15] Young and his wave theory probably would have been forgotten by the time of the 1834 *Report* had it not been for the subsequent work done in France. In 1819 the French Academy of Science not only agreed to publish a paper on the wave theory but it awarded that paper first prize in the Academy's competition for that year. When a paper was "crowned" as this one was, it signified acceptance of the theory to an extent beyond anything Young had been granted in England. The author of the French *Memoir* was Augustin Jean Fresnel.

The wave theory of light is now usually known as the Young-Fresnel theory. The inventors of the theory had careers that contrasted in many ways. Fresnel, born in Broglie, France, in 1788, was buffeted by the Revolution; and Young, who lived in the relatively tranquil early nineteenth century England, was unaffected by political change and, as far as is known, had no political preferences. Fresnel could barely read by the age of eight and never did have a taste for language study. He had what would be called numerical sense in that he was competent at mathematics and became an engineer; whereas Young had a literary sense, as seen by his facility with many languages, his career as an Egyptologist, and the amount and variety of his publications. Young never seemed to be in want of money or position, and Fresnel was plagued all his life by difficulty in obtaining both.

Fresnel's father was an architect and at sixteen the son entered *Ecole Polytechnique*. While at the *Polytechnique,* Fresnel distinguished himself in mathematics under the instruction of Adrien Marie Legendre. After graduation Fresnel became a government civil engineer, which was to be his profession for the rest of his life. His first appointment was in the department of Vendée, where he worked until Napoleon's brief return to power in 1815. Fresnel opposed Napoleon's return and as a result lost his position at Vendée. The Revolution, therefore, affected Fresnel's life in two important ways. The *Polytechnique* was founded as a result of the Revolution and were it not for the policy of the school, young men without means, like Fresnel, could not have gotten the excellent mathematical and technical training that became available there after 1794. The losing of the job in Vendée was a disguised benefit for Fresnel. His friend and scientific collaborator François Arago obtained a job for Fresnel in Paris, where he worked as a government engineer and had time for his investigations on light.

France's scientific academy was suspended briefly (1793-1795); it had its name changed (1795-1816) and its members were harassed by the government. In spite of all this, it remained the leading scientific society through the Revolution and the succeeding years. Cordial relations existed between Napoleon and the members of the *Institut National.* It was principally because of Napoleon's belief in the value of science that the Academy not only survived the Revolution but flourished during those unsettled years of the Revolution and afterwards. The Academy was therefore able to provide a forum for new and controversial ideas like Fresnel's. The French government's support of science had a stifling effect in the long run (see

Chapter Eleven, "The Encouragement and Diffusion of Science"),
but in the early decades of the nineteenth century there was no
other forum of consequence. In England the anemic Royal
Society never did warm up enough to supply a forum for controversy on light. By the time the British Association was
founded, the controversy was over as far as scientists of that day
were concerned. The French Academy did not simply listen to
Fresnel's ideas on the wave theory in polite silence. The members
of the Academy fought over the theory, and there is no healthier
climate for a new theory. Fresnel's progress in the study of light
was rapid and, like Young's, was relatively brief. The whole of
Fresnel's work covered a period of a little over a decade from
1815 to 1826.

The judges who chose Fresnel's paper for the Academy's
"crown" in 1819 included Laplace, Biot, and Poisson. These men
had stoutly opposed the wave theory. Laplace was a Newtonian,
his *Mechanique Celeste* constituted a valuable supplement to
Newtonian mechanics; and Biot had developed a theory of light
based on particles. Their recommendation for an award to Fresnel did not signify that they accepted the theory, just that the
idea was worthy of notice. The Academy did not print Fresnel's
prize paper until 1826, which was a seven-year delay. Some
writers attribute the delay to the continuing opposition in the
Academy to the wave theory.[16] There is no doubt that the
opposition did continue for a time, but it also should be remembered that the Academy was notoriously slow in publishing
papers. (Fourier's crown memoir of 1811 was not published until
1824.)

In 1827 Sir John Herschel complained that Fresnel's paper of
1821, which first proposed that light had transverse vibrations,
had yet to be published. Herschel knew that the French
Academy had recommended the publication of the paper.[17]
Fresnel, Whewell wrote, "appears by this time to have sought
other channels of publication." The *Annales de Chimie et de
Physique* published a paper by Fresnel on refraction.

Arago, Fresnel's strongest supporter, faltered sometimes, it was
said, because of the opposition he had to face in the Academy
and because Arago, to the end, never could accept Fresnel's idea
of transverse vibrations, which was central to the whole theory.[18]

Further evidence of the Academy's coolness to Fresnel is the report on his 1822 paper on double refraction. The commission that passed on the memoir consisted of Arago, Fourier, and Ampère. They found that "it would be impossible for them to pronounce at present a decided judgment"; but added, "they have not thought it right to delay any longer making known a work" of such great difficulty and which exhibited a brilliant "talent for experiment and the spirit of invention."[19]

The French Academy of Science deserves the main credit for the acceptance and diffusion of Fresnel's theory. True, there was strong opposition on the part of some members to the theory and even strong supporters, like Arago, wavered sometime; in addition, the Academy delayed publication of Fresnel's papers. But the fact is that the Academy did listen, did dispute, and it gave Fresnel's memoir a "crown" to signify that at least it was worthy of serious consideration. Had there not been the spreading of the news of the theory through the reverberations within the Academy, it is unlikely that Sir John Herschel would have heard of Fresnel so that he could complain that he was not hearing enough. That Fresnel was "driven" to seek other outlets for his publication may very well have been due to the Academy's inexcusable laxity in publication. But there is no question that the scientific journals would not have considered Fresnel's work were it not for the fact that the Academy had thought it an important hypothesis. The conclusion is that it is not enough that an established scientific institution, like the French Academy or the Royal Society, give a polite hearing to a new theory. (Young was listened to politely enough.) The institution or society must consider the idea worth arguing over, and the vibrations from the ensuing controversy diffuse new theories through the scientific community. How fortunate Fresnel was to have the strong opposition of Laplace, Biot, and Poisson. Young's misfortune was not so much that he lacked support but that no scientist in England took him seriously enough to argue with him. Brougham does not count.

Say what you will about the *Académie des Sciences*, that it was bungling, inefficient, and quarrelsome, but add that it did serve as a forum for new ideas during the early part of the nineteenth century. In England, on the other hand, Whewell reported that there was "no visible body of men, fitted by their knowledge and character to pronounce judgment on such a question, or to give the proper impulse and bias to public opinion." As for the Royal Society, the French Academy's counterpart, Whewell ruled it out because it "had not, for a long time, by custom or institution, possessed or aimed at such functions."[20]

Fresnel had not known of Young's work when he began his researches. When he was made aware of the earlier work, Fresnel unhesitatingly gave Young the credit due him. But Fresnel did more than rediscover Young. The English historian Merz wrote that Fresnel's "work lay . . . in combining a number of fruitful suggestions thrown out by contemporary or earlier writers into a consistent whole, correcting and enlarging them as was found necessary, and following them out into their logical consequences."[21]

In his 1819 memoir, Fresnel said that Young had first introduced the principle of interference into optics but that Young had only considered the limiting cases of maximum and minimum interference. By considering the two extremes Young was able to explain the colors of thin plates but, Fresnel wrote, Young "has not computed the intensity of the light for any intermediate cases or for any number whatever of trains of waves, as I here propose to do." The principle that two sources of light can produce waves that differ by more or less than one-half wave length is known as *phase difference*. The idea of phase difference as Fresnel saw it followed naturally from the wave theory itself. But it was Fresnel who made this deduction so clear and demonstrated its usefulness.

Fresnel also conceived of the idea of dividing a wave front of light into geometrical parts known as *zones*. This device enabled Fresnel to explain how light was propagated rectilinearly or as rays when it was composed of waves. The ideas of phase and of zones could be used to explain geometrically one of the remaining mysteries of light, that is, diffraction. Diffraction was the result of passing a ray of light by a sharp straight edge. Outside of the shadow of the straight edge, there appeared bands of light and shadow known as *fringes*. Neither the partisans of the wave theory nor those of the particle theory had devised a satisfactory explanation of diffraction. For the first time Fresnel had produced such an explanation using the wave theory and the ideas of phase and zones.

Fresnel did not withhold credit that he thought his predecessors deserved. It was perhaps this generosity that deceived some into underestimating his contribution. Fresnel said that Huygens had simply overlooked certain aspects of the wave theory. This oversight "prevented him [Huygens] from discovering the phenomena of diffraction," which he could have deduced from his theory without recourse to experiment. The ideas of phase and zones were not in conflict, were indeed in agreement, with the wave theory of light, but that does not mean that phase and zones were obvious outcomes of the theory.

Fresnel's presentation of his ideas was in marked contrast with Young's. There was no reverential tone in Fresnel's papers and no attempt to demonstrate that Newton was not far off from the wave theory. Fresnel saw how the adherence to the Newtonian particle theory of light led to unreasonable suppositions: "If one adopts the Newtonian theory," Fresnel wrote, "he is tempted at first to explain the exterior fringes as produced by a force which is alternately attractive and repulsive. . . . I shall now consider the consequences of this theory and show that its results are not justified by experiment. . . ." The consequences were: *"the phenomena of diffraction cannot be explained on the emission-theory."*[22]

The polarization of light had not been satisfactorily explained by using the wave theory up to Fresnel's time. Newton had suggested that polarization of light was due to the stream of particles assuming a flattened shape with sides. By the time the 1819 memoir was published, Fresnel had arrived at an explanation for polarized light that harmonized with the wave theory. In a footnote to the memoir, Fresnel wrote, "I have become convinced since the writing of this memoir that light vibrations are at right angles to the rays. . . ."[23]

The wave theory of light owed much of its conceptualization to the well-understood theory of sound. The analogy with sound had been useful to Young and was used by most followers of that theory. Sound waves, it was well-known, vibrated along the line of the propagation of sound. Now Fresnel was suggesting that light, unlike sound, vibrated perpendicularly to the line of propagation, and thereby he was able to explain polarization. Was this an extra and unwarranted hypothesis? Arago, who was collaborating with Fresnel, thought so. Arago balked at the idea. One of their experiments on polarized light had produced an unexpected result, and Fresnel insisted that transverse vibrations were the only possible "translation of this fact into the undulatory theory"; whereupon Arago "protested that he had not the courage to publish such a conception," and accordingly the transverse vibration of light theory was published under Fresnel's name alone.[24]

By 1834 the wave theory was in the ascendency. Not that by that time it had been proven *true*. The wave theory was established by that time because it had met the test of acceptability set by nineteenth century scientists. William Whewell, when he wrote his *History of the Inductive Sciences* in 1847, expressed the attitude of the day. "In the undulatory [wave] theory," he wrote, ". . . all tends to unity and simplicity." Truth, he believed, had this character. He went on to summarize the strengths of the wave theory:

> We explain reflection and refraction by undulations [and point by point this theory explains all known phenomena]. Polarization for a moment checks us; but not long; for the direction of our vibrations is hitherto arbitrary;—we allow polarization to decide it. Having done this for the sake of polarization, we find that it also answers an entirely different purpose, that of giving the law of double refraction.

Since "unity and simplicity" were the test of a theory, the particle theory was obviously ruled out. "Such a theory may, to a certain extent, explain the phenomena which it was at first contrived to meet;" Whewell insisted, "but every new class of facts requires a new supposition,—an addition to the machinery; and as observation goes on, these incoherent appendages accumulate, till they overwhelm and upset the original framework." He concluded: "This is not the character of truth." The particle theory had lost its appeal to scientists not merely because it was awkward but because the continual addition of corollaries made it no longer appear as *a* theory but as several theories strung together. This stringing together of supposition after supposition was counter to what was believed to be the function of a theory, that was, to provide a simple explanation for as broad a group of phenomena as possible. The many phenomena of light, reflection, refraction, diffraction, and polarization had to be explained by one theory, not by a collection of loosely related concepts.

The ability of the wave theory to account for all of these phenomena was an irresistible claim to assent. "Truth may give rise to such a coincidence; falsehood cannot," Whewell wrote. He emphasized that the number and complexity of the phenomena of light could not disturb the wave theory. "It makes not a single new physical hypothesis; but out of its original stock of principles it educes the counterpart of all that observation shows."[25]

The British Association "Report" on the present state of physical optics that was given in 1834 explained why the wave theory was acceptable then. The author concluded his "Report" on light by observing that "any well-imagined theory may be accommodated to phenomena, and seem to explain them, if only we increase the number of its *postulates,* so as still to embrace each new class of phenomena as it arises." Truth, as we have seen, was defined differently. "In a certain sense, and to a certain extent, such a theory may be said to be true, so far as it is the mere expression of known laws. But it is no longer a *physical theory,* whose very essence it is to connect these laws together, and to demonstrate their dependence on some higher principle: —it is an aggregate of separate principles, whose mutual relations are unknown."[26]

What was evolving in the nineteenth century through the renewed efforts to deal with phenomena like light, heat, and electricity, was a drastic change in outlook. One might say that the nineteenth century was a period when the search for the universal law of nature was gradually abandoned. Scientists were not conscious of the change in method of arriving at theories, and few noted the trend in the change of the nature of the theories. There was much to be done in studying the implications of the new ideas of the nature of heat, light, and electricity. Towards the end of the century, some scientists who had turned philosophers, such as William Whewell, Henri Poincaré, and Pierre Duhem, were describing and noting the changes in the philosophy of science that had taken place. The so-called revolution in physics of the twentieth century was actually the enunciation of the implications of the philosophical changes brought about in the nineteenth century. The twentieth century science, when seen historically, was not a break with the past but a continuation of it.

If anyone made a break with the past, it was the nineteenth century scientists. Theirs was, without many being aware of it, a break with the philosophy of science as developed by the men of the scientific revolution, such as Galileo, Descartes, and Newton. The scientific revolution had distinguished between primary and secondary qualities as a means of arriving at the true nature of the physical world. The sense of touch, smell, odor, color, and the like, were subjective and therefore deceiving. These were secondary qualities; they could not be quantified or described mathematically and therefore were not a way to arrive at a description of the world as it was. The primary qualities, mass, extension, force, things that could be measured and described mathematically, were the only ways of perceiving truth. The method to be used was mathematics and experiment, but as experiment was invoked only to demonstrate what had already been discovered by mathematical deduction, experiment played a secondary role. (Galileo's experiments on freely falling bodies are a good example. They were performed *after* he had deduced the law of freely falling bodies, mathematically.) Two things that were established during the seventeenth century and that were to undergo change in the nineteenth century were that the object of science was to arrive at absolute truth and the method of arriving there was to be mathematically deduced and experimentally demonstrated.

Nineteenth century scientists found the methods of the seventeenth century inadequate. Contrast the experiments performed by Joule, Fresnel, and Faraday with those performed by Galileo and Newton. Galileo used experiment to demonstrate, and Newton's best experiments, those on light, were data-gathering expeditions. Newton found many interesting new facts about light, such as the multifarious composition of white light. But his theory of light was an awkward attempt to bind together these seemingly unrelated facts. Fresnel's experiments were an attempt to devise a theory experimentally. Joule's work lies somewhere between discovering new facts and developing a theory. Faraday's work unquestionably comes under the heading of developing new theories by means of experiment. But the nineteenth century did not substitute experiment for mathematics.

In an attempt to describe the relation between things, that is, to develop theories that would simplify the observed phenomena, scientists gave up the attempt to discover absolute truth and undertook rather to draw a picture of that part of the world as perceived by man. Such an attempt required more resourcefulness, more imagination, and caution.

The imaginative work of constructing progressed by the use of mathematics or experiment. Instead of the traditional seventeenth century approach of mathematics and experiment, the nineteenth century used alternately mathematics or experiment. This procedure was a result of the national differences in the training for science and the pursuit of science in the first part of the nineteenth century. British scientists were self-taught, and what men like Dalton, Joule, and Young could teach themselves were techniques for conducting experiments. Whatever training they had in mathematics was not in mathematical physics. The mathematics they learned in school or university was "pure" mathematics without reference to science. The British scientist therefore developed his theories by means of experiment and by use of models. He then used mathematics, if at all, to test the validity of the experiment.

French scientists received formal training in such schools as *Ecole Polytechnique* with a strong tradition of mathematical physics. Science was taught in France through the use of mathematical logic. French scientists therefore approached science as mathematicians, and the British, as experimentalists. This statement was generally, although not universally, true in the first half of the century and the distinction gradually disappeared. As an example of this distinction we have seen how Young arrived at the wave theory of light through his experiments with sound and light. He has been criticized for his poor mathematical presentation. Fresnel's mathematics, on the other hand, was elegant. His experiments were mathematically conceived and were described in his paper by geometrical constructions. Compare that with Young's use of the analogy of audio "beats" and light interference.

Much of the controversy between the British and the French was due to this diversity in view. This alternation in approach produced progress, whereas most were only aware of controversy. New concepts developed mathematically by an Ampère were elaborated experimentally by a Faraday using a distinctly British approach. The theory of light crossed the Channel in the other direction, going from Young to Fresnel.

Out of this difference of viewpoint developed a new outlook. Obviously there was not one path to truth. The experience in developing the wave theory of light had been instructive. Poincaré derived philosophical implications from the result. "The theory called the theory of undulations [wave theory] forms a complete whole, which is satisfying to the mind," he wrote, "but we must not ask from it what it cannot give us. The object of mathematical theories is not to reveal to us the real nature of things; that would be an unreasonable claim." His conclusion, written in 1907, was: "Now, we daily see what science is doing for us . . . the aim of science is not things themselves . . . but the relations between things; outside those relations there is no reality knowable."[27]

What was happening to the search for the unity in nature which all scientists sought? Truth, or the attempt to discover the whole fabric of nature, was abandoned. Duhem said at the end of the century that "every physicist naturally aspires to the unity of science."[28] But the unity of science was quite a different thing from discovering the unity of nature and this scientists were coming to realize by the end of the century. Merz described the new outlook as beginning around the middle of the century. The search, he wrote, was for a general term "under which the different terms could be comprised, which would give a still higher generalisation, a more complete unification of knowledge." What was the "greatest of all exact generalisations"? It was "the conception of energy."[29]

Even though this grand generalization did not begin to take shape until the end of the century, to someone like Grove the relationship was clear as early as 1842. In a paper entitled "The Correlation and Conservation of Forces," Grove wrote: "Light, Heat, Electricity, Magnetism, Motion, and Chemical-affinity, are all convertible material affections. . . . Cause and effect, therefore, in their abstract relation to these forces, are words solely of convenience: we are totally unacquainted with the ultimate generating power of each and all of them, and probably shall ever remain so . . . we must . . . content ourselves with studying their effects and developing by experiment their mutual relations."[30]

Dynamical Chemistry

8   Was chemistry a science by mid-century? In 1860 Cannizzaro's *Sketch* had harmonized the various aspects of the atomic theory and in 1869 Mendeleev's periodic table had shown that there was a pattern to atomic weights. Both of these events provided a means of summarizing and classifying what was known about chemical substances. They introduced a period of experimentation. Chemical theory was scientific insofar as it led to further experiment.

There was dissent from this view. Marcellin Berthelot published a book, *Essai de Mechanique Chimique,* in 1874. The book was widely read. Berthelot wanted to work out for chemistry "principles of a new science, more general and more abstract than the description of individual properties. . . ." At that time, he claimed, chemists were not able to determine "the properties themselves of all of these substances, or the forces which are exerted between them." Chemistry must cease being, Berthelot said, merely one of the "descriptive sciences." It must reach the "ideal condition," that is, of a true science, "by connecting its principles and its problems with those of the purely physical and mechanical sciences."[1]

There was never any argument with Berthelot's idea that the "end in view" of every science was greater generality. How to get it? Chemists had an immediate problem of what to make of the data as it began to flood in upon them. Theories were developed that would help them organize all of the compounds into some order, but each theory fell under the welter of data. On top of that dilemma, it was found that animal and vegetable life revealed a whole new area of compounds, organic compounds. This discovery at first seemed to destroy any hope for wider generality in chemical theory but eventually provided a key to a broader theory.

Another type of generality in chemistry was introduced towards the end of the century by Josiah Willard Gibbs. Gibbs took concepts of another science, thermodynamics, and applied or superimposed them on chemistry. These calipers as a new instrument of measurement and description did not produce the "new science" that Berthelot hoped for, but it did give a radically new aspect to chemistry.

In the early nineteenth century, some substances, such as animal and vegetable products, were considered outside of chemistry. But some of these organic substances were involved in chemical processes, the production of soap from animal fat and the manufacture of potash from wood, for example. Nevertheless, it was believed the organic substances were unique. Chemists could not compound them. Only living organisms could add the essential "vital force." But could these compounds be analyzed in the same way as inorganic substances?

The response to this question was not only that it could be done but that it should be done. The theory of combination developed in the study of inorganic compounds could be "the key," Berzelius wrote in 1817, "by which we may hope to arrive at true ideas with respect to the composition of organic substances."[2] There appeared also to be a useful similarity between organic and inorganic reactions. Lavoisier had shown that the inorganic processes of combustion and oxidation were related to the organic phenomenon of respiration.

In 1823 Justus Liebig found that his analysis of silver fulminate, an organic substance, indicated that it had exactly the same composition as another organic compound, silver cyanate, which had been analyzed by Friedrich Wöhler. Liebig, after he convinced himself that Wöhler had not made an error, accepted the fact that it was possible to have two compounds with entirely different properties but the same composition.

It appeared therefore that organic compounds were going to be difficult to analyze. Examples of these oddly related substances began to multiply. Faraday found a hydrocarbon in oil gas, in 1825, which had the same composition as the known organic compound ethylene. Then in 1828 Wöhler was astounded to find that he could artificially produce urea from a like compound of cyanate of ammonia. Wöhler's discovery was to have an impact on biological theory since he had artificially produced a substance that all believed could only be produced in a living organism by means of a "vital" force.

Berzelius remained skeptical of these discoveries until he had conducted some confirming experiments. It was he who coined the word *isomer* for organic substances that had the same chemical composition but different properties. Could isomerism only occur in the organic world? Apparently this was the case.

The discovery of numerous isomers in organic chemistry led to an attempt to formulate a theory or classification system around them. One such attempt was a comparison with a similar type of inorganic compound. But this attempt proved unsatisfactory because the groups of compounds appeared highly contrived, and it became necessary to invent fictitious substances. By considering only organic substances, a pattern appeared in several different groups of compounds. Each group could be identified by the fact that it had exactly the same amount of two or more elements. These elements seemed to behave in chemical reactions as if they were a single element. Combinations of elements such as these were called *radicals*.

In 1832 Liebig and Wöhler published a paper, "Ueber das Radikal der Benzoesaure" (Upon the Radical of Benzoic Acid), which claimed to have discovered what was named a "compound element" in a series of organic compounds. This radical, or compound element, appeared in a variety of substances without alteration. It was called *Benzoyl* and its composition was given as $C_{14}H_{10}O_2$.

Five years later, in 1837, Liebig collaborated on a paper with

Jean Baptiste André Dumas, which reported a broad series of experiments on organic compounds using the point of view of the radical theory. Their findings indicated, they thought, that at last the chemical definition of organic compound could be given. They wrote that organic chemistry was, in fact, the *Chemistry of Compound Radicals*.[3] The radical theory stimulated a whole fresh series of experiments. Such well-known chemists as Gay-Lussac, Robert Bunsen, Liebig, Dumas, and Wöhler helped develop the new theory.

Justus Liebig's work as teacher, writer, editor, and original researcher closely connects him with the history of nineteenth century chemistry.

His interest in the laboratory began in his father's dye works. As a school boy, Liebig had a brief and unsuccessful career. He was then apprenticed to an apothecary. The association was unsatisfactory to both the boy and his master, who ended the apprenticeship when Liebig blew out an attic window-sash during an experiment. At age sixteen Liebig was without training. His knowledge consisted of a scattering of things that he had learned in the course of undirected reading. Nevertheless, he entered the University of Bonn, which had just been founded. He left Bonn for Erlangen to follow the only chemistry professor he found of worth. He received a Ph.D. from the University of Erlangen.

His education was still not satisfactory, for as Liebig said, "it was then a wretched time for chemistry" in Germany. He therefore took the route that many German chemists of his generation took. Liebig went to Paris and there put in another apprenticeship, but this time with a sympathetic master, Gay-Lussac.

In 1824 Liebig returned to Germany to accept an appointment as professor of chemistry at the little-known University of Giessen. It was in such a place that a young man could innovate. At Giessen, Liebig started the first teaching laboratory of chemistry in Germany. Young men came from all over the world, for here chemists were vigorously exploring the frontiers in experimental chemistry.

The instruction at Giessen was individualistic. Liebig assigned each advanced student a project and he then supervised the work by daily criticism of the progress reports. Twice a week

Liebig met with the students to discuss what he considered the most important work done by both himself and the students. The result was a constant interchange of new information, lively discussions, and the kind of supervision that corrects and encourages the performance of original work. This model of advanced scientific education, which was an advance on the single master-student relationship, soon spread to every country. It has since become the standard procedure for graduate education in all of the sciences, but it was begun by a young man who clearly saw what was needed because of his own difficulty in obtaining an education.

Liebig emphasized the experimental approach, but he explicitly distinguished between the practical and the theoretical. In a letter to Faraday in 1844, Liebig remarked on the "practical tendency" of English chemists who neglected "purely scientific works." Liebig added that "practice alone can never lead to the discovery of a truth or a principle." Liebig went on to complain that in Germany only a trifling value was placed on practical results. "For both nations," Liebig wrote, "the golden medium would certainly be a real good fortune."[4]

The University of Erlangen had a strong positive and negative effect on Liebig. His close friendship and long conversations with the accomplished German poet, A. von Platen, was supposed to have helped Liebig "to place a true value on the study of history and languages, and was thereby enabled to fill up gaps in his general education."[5]

On the other hand, Liebig wrote with rancor of his more formal experience at Erlangen:

> I myself spent a portion of my student days at a university where the greatest philosopher and metaphysician of the century charmed the thoughtful youth around him into admiration and imitation; who could at that time resist the contagion? I, too, have lived through this period—a period so rich in words and ideas and so poor in true knowledge and genuine studies. . .

He finished with the bitterest words known to man: "it cost me two precious years of my life."[6]

Perhaps an older Liebig looked back on this part of his experience as an intellectual tempering. The point is that Liebig was a literary man too and he could not have developed that talent in the laboratory. His writing exhibited, it was said, "the capacity of the true investigator to state points correctly and clearly . . . and to draw able and ingenious conclusions. These merits impart to Liebig's writings, which show a characteristic power of language, a great and ever-renewed charm."[7] Liebig's productivity as a writer and editor was amazing and the number of his publications gives some measure of his influence in the nineteenth century.

In 1832 Liebig founded a journal called *Annalen der Chemie und Pharmacie,* which published reports of work done by Liebig and his students at Giessen. This lifelong labor as editor produced 165 volumes. In addition, he collaborated with Wöhler and Poggendorff on a dictionary of pure and applied chemistry. Add to this his books and articles on the chemistry of agriculture and physiology, and a newspaper column. This column, *Familiar Letters on Chemistry,* was in the nineteenth century tradition of popularization of science by leading men of science. All told, Liebig published 318 separate papers, in addition to his editing works and his books.

A striking feature of Liebig's work was his successful collaboration with other chemists. His collaboration with Wöhler began more in the spirit of friendship than from professional necessity. Wöhler wrote to Liebig in 1829 that "we might, for the humour of it, undertake some chemical work together." In that manner a long, friendly, and productive series of collaborations between the two was begun. Liebig did important experimental work with Dumas, too, and shared literary chores with Wöhler, Hermann Kopp, and Poggendorff.

In his willingness to collaborate with others on scientific enterprises, Liebig was not unusual. Another well-known team was Auguste Laurent and Charles Gerhardt. Collaboration between chemists was more common than between physicists. We find William Thomson serving as mentor to Maxwell but never collaborating on a project. Thomson's collaboration with P.G. Tait in the writing of a text was unsatisfactory. Tait was constantly exhorting Thomson, and the work was not completed. In fact, competition, which excludes the sharing of confidences, rather than cooperation, appears to be the general rule in the history of science.

Why the exceptions in nineteenth century chemistry? The answer seems to be that chemistry was undergoing a radical change in theoretical approach and simultaneously was venturing into such new areas as agriculture and physiology. Collaboration was more common among talents than division of a big job. As an example of joining forces, there was Liebig's pharmacy background with Wöhler's medical one. Scientists today place much value on "having-someone-to-talk-to"; but outside of the few exceptions in organic chemistry, which was mostly carried on through the mails, there is little historical evidence that collaboration leads to original work. That is not to say that cooperative ventures and association with one's peers is of no value. Work at Giessen and at the Cavendish laboratories has been the start of many brilliant careers in science. But once started, the really creative men required no more outside stimulation than could be obtained by letters or through annual meetings of the scientific societies.

Liebig believed in the need for practical application of science. It was to be expected that he would seek to apply his theoretical work in organic chemistry to physiology and agriculture. When Liebig turned to the study of agricultural chemistry around 1838, so little work was being done that it scarcely warranted being called a field. No serious work on the chemical basis of plant growth had been done since Humphry Davy's lectures on the "Elements of Agricultural Chemistry," which were delivered annually between 1802 and 1812. A chemist interested in agricultural chemistry had to contend with well-worn, widely-believed, and unproven ideas. For example, it was commonly believed that humus was the universal nutrient of plants. Liebig's investigations, which were supported by his students' experiments, indicated that humus, an organic substance, did not contribute directly to plant nutrition. Instead, he wrote: "The nutritive materials of all green plants are inorganic substances." The source of plant growth was commonly recognized inorganic compounds. "Plants live upon carbonic acid, ammonia (nitric acid), water, phosphoric acid, sulphuric acid, silicic acid, lime, magnesia, potash, and iron; many of them also require common salt."

Liebig declared that not only were humus and organic substances not needed for growth but organic substances must be broken down to inorganic compounds before they could be absorbed by plants. "Dung, the excrementa of the lower animals and of man, does not act upon plant life through (the direct assimilation of) its organic elements, but indirectly through the products of its decomposition- and putrification-processes, i.e., by the transformation of its carbon into carbonic acid, and of its nitrogen into ammonia or nitric acid. Organic manure, which consists of portions or *débris* of plants and animals, may be replaced by the inorganic compounds into which it breaks up in the ground."[8]

These ideas appeared in Liebig's *Chemistry in its Application to Agriculture and Physiology* (1840). The next step up the biological ladder for Liebig was the nutrition of animals and man. His report on "Organic Chemistry Applied to Physiology and Pathology" was reviewed for the British Association for the Advancement of Science in 1842. The picture of nature as described by Liebig appeared remarkably uncomplicated.

"How beautifully simple, then, by the aid of these discoveries, does nutrition appear!" This exclamation was made by the man who reported Liebig's findings to the British Association. The now familiar cycle of life was introduced: "In point of fact, then *vegetables* produce in their organism the blood of *all animals;* for the carnivora, in consuming the blood and flesh of the graminivora [grain eaters], consume, strictly speaking, the vegetable principles which have served for the nourishment of the latter."[9]

As Liebig saw life, there was an "infinite series of organic products which begins with the inorganic food of plants, and extends to the most complex constituents of the nervous system and brain of animals, the highest in the scale, we see no blank, no interruption." To Liebig, food not only was the basis for growth, "plastic food," but also supplied the heat energy to warm the body and produced the energy of motion.

Liebig's contribution to physiology was the introduction of the method and knowledge of chemistry. This type of relation between sciences was common, Liebig pointed out. By absorbing parts of physics, chemistry had assumed its modern character. "Exactly in the same way," he wrote, in *Familiar Letters*, "the more accurate knowledge of vital phenomena will establish the conviction that a number of physiological properties depend on chemical composition; and physiology, when it shall have taken up animal chemistry as a part of itself, will possess the means of investigating this relation of dependence," that is, the dependence of physiological properties on chemical composition.

The other side of the life cycle from growth and action was the return of animal life to the soil where it became plant food. The return to the soil, decay, was a type of oxidation. Decay and fermentation were related, according to Liebig, because decay was "a process of combustion taking place at common temperatures, in which the products of the fermentation [the first stage in decay] and putrefaction of plants and of animal bodies combine gradually with the oxygen of the atmosphere."[10] Liebig's theory of fermentation and putrefaction preceded Louis Pasteur's. Liebig had not opposed the idea of a vital force, but he chose to do without it where possible. Pasteur's theory of fermentation was a modification of the vitalist view because it introduced *animocules* to explain a chemical change.

Organic chemistry not only was useful in studying life processes but analysis of these compounds tempted chemists to form new theories of chemical composition. One of these theories, the substitution theory, was first described by Jean Baptiste André Dumas in 1835. Compounds, according to this theory, could be classified by the reactions into which they entered. This method contrasted with the other method of describing compounds by means of their constituents. Dumas discovered that acetic acid could be produced from vinegar and that acetic acid was "chlorinated vinegar" because chlorine had replaced the hydrogen in the vinegar.

"Here then is a new organic acid," he wrote, "containing a very considerable quantity of chlorine, and exhibiting none of the reactions of chlorine . . . and yet this remarkable substitution has produced only a slight change in its physical properties, all its essential characters remaining unaltered."[11]

This discovery led Dumas to investigate other organic compounds for similar behavior. He concluded that when any compound containing hydrogen was exposed to the action of chlorine, bromine, or iodine, the compound took up an equal volume of chlorine, bromine, or iodine for each atom of hydrogen lost.

It was Auguste Laurent, another Frenchman, who saw more in Dumas' discovery than the simplification of chemical reactions by grouping them together. Laurent noted that it was possible to produce a new compound by substituting chlorine for hydrogen and that this substitution does not materially alter the chemical character of the original compound. Laurent's substitution theory held that chlorine took over the role of hydrogen in a replacement, and the exchange did not alter the properties of the compound.

Laurent derived a system of classifying compounds which he compared with botanical classification. What if, he asked, "we might some day succeed in discovering, that all the parts of the same plant contain something in common . . . which . . . will enable us to understand why they are capable of transforming themselves into one another?"

The substitution theory presented chemists with a "something in common" that could be used for grouping compounds. "I have endeavored to ascertain," Laurent wrote, "whether there is not in all the different parts of our chemical tree, something . . . which would enable us to understand, why all these compounds can reciprocally engender one another."[12] But the substitution theory failed under the necessity of classifying the great number and variety of organic substances which were henceforth considered chemical compounds. The next attempt at classification was the type theory.

Jean Dumas concluded that "there are in organic chemistry certain types which remain unchanged, even when their hydrogen is replaced by an equal amount of chlorine, bromine, or iodine." For example, acetic acid and trichloracetic acids, aldehyde and chloral, marsh gas and chloroform, belong severally to the same chemical types. In 1853 Charles Gerhardt simplified this idea. Organic compounds, he believed, could be related to three or four types: water (H_2O), hydrogen (H_2), hydrochloric acid (HCl), and ammonia (H_3N). Just as

Mendeleev was to use atomic weights in such a way that elements of like properties were grouped together, Gerhardt used types of chemical properties to group organic compounds. "It can be seen . . . how the application of the notion of series permits simplication of the general theory of organic compounds," Gerhardt wrote. "They no longer terrify by their number and variety . . . they become simply terms whose properties can be predicted according to the place they occupy in the series."[13]

The type theory was a convenience, a method for cataloguing compounds, which in no way, according to Gerhardt, was supposed to be a theory of the actual structure itself. Many chemists accepted the theory on that basis, and the general view was that even though the theory did not bring them closer to truth it did, in Liebig's words, have "utility."

Was that enough to commend a theory? Hermann Kolbe thought the new theory "nothing but a vain artifice." Why, he asked, would Nature restrict herself to only three types?[14] These words may have reminded chemists of Robert Boyle inveighing against limiting the study of chemistry, in the seventeenth century, to three or four elements.

The substitution-type theories contradicted the dualistic theory of chemical combination. The dualistic theory explained the force of chemical combination by likening it to the positive and negative forces of electricity. But the substitution theory showed that an electropositive substance could be substituted for an electronegative one and therefore it directly contradicted the dualistic theory.

The supporters of the type-substitution theory were known as the "modern" or "French" school. They were criticized by those who held fast to the Berzelius-dualistic theory as "having introduced a purely formal systematisation according to merely external differences." By ignoring electro-chemical phenomena, it was charged, "the 'modern' school lost the only remaining chance of explaining, and not classifying merely, chemical phenomena."[15]

Neither the dualistic nor the type-substitution theorists could be completely correct. Each had its errors. Disagreement over what a theory should be and what it should do was more seriously divisive than the theories themselves. Some still insisted that exact science had truth and it had to be general. The attempt at Karlsruhe to establish *the true* atomic theory contrasted with the discussions on physical questions. Chemists were under the illusion that in physics, that exact science, agreement was universal and truth established. They were not reading the lessons of the controversies in physics correctly. The particle versus the wave theory of light dispute and the action-at-a-distance versus medium theory dispute in electricity did not result in an absolute triumph of one over the other. The resultant theory that emerged was more likely a combination (Ampère *plus* Faraday) that was useful in understanding the phenomena and in doing further work. Maxwell had said that it was always better to have at least two ways of looking at phenomena. The supporters of the wave theory considered their strongest argument to be that it was the least awkward and did not have to resort to several postulates.

Another hope of chemists was that one day they would be able to establish General Principles. Presumably a Newton would do for chemistry what *the* Newton had done for physics: produce universal laws. A historian of chemistry, Hermann Kopp, wrote in 1873: "No theory has as yet been formed in chemistry which, starting from a definite principle, attempts to deduce results of experience as necessary consequences."

Was he voicing the dissatisfaction of the majority of chemists when he added: "The doctrines which have been termed in chemistry theoretical are still only such as permit us to bring connection into the results which practical chemistry has gained in special directions; or to form a picture how we might think of them mutually related."[16]

Instead of a note of discontent Kopp should have sounded pleased. What he had said was that chemistry had worked out a technique for successful theory building. The rules were to reduce the phenomena to their simplest principles and to expand the theories by means of additional data to show its relationship with other phenomena. That was exactly what theory was supposed to do, "bring connection into the results of practical chemistry," that is, observation. Theory was supposed to help take the facts and "to form a picture how we might think of them as mutually related."

In 1852 Edward Frankland communicated the results of his experiments in "organo-metallic compounds" to the Royal Society. The hypothesis that he had formed was "that the •atoms of zinc, tin, arsenic, antimony etc., had only room, so to speak, for the attachment of a fixed and definite number of the atoms of other elements. . . ."[17] This hypothesis was an important extension of the atomic theory and the laws of constant and multiple proportions. These laws stated that elements combined in the same or constant proportion by weight, and these proportions were related to each other by multiples of small whole numbers. These theories had ample experimental evidence to support them, but there was as yet no explanation as to why the atoms combined in this particular way.

Frankland now suggested that this constancy of proportion was the result of properties of the atoms. One element had room only for a fixed number of atoms of other elements. The determining factor was the ability of atoms to attach to other atoms. This idea as it developed became known as *the doctrine of atomicity* or *atom linking*.

Friedrich August Kekulé discovered that one element, carbon, had extraordinary binding powers or atomicity. He wrote, in a paper published in 1858, that "the sum of the chemical units of the elements, combined with one atom of carbon is always equal to four," or as he said, carbon was "tetratomic."[18] This concept opened the way for a fruitful period in the investigation of carbon compounds. One after another of these complicated substances were subjected to successful chemical analysis. It was found that the common element in all organic compounds was carbon and it was carbon's ability to attach to many other elements, and to itself, that gave all carbon compounds their peculiar stamp. Organic chemistry was found to be the study of carbon compounds.

The idea of atom linking led the chemists to diagram the chains of atoms. The diagram idea evolved into a structure theory in which the force of attraction became a foundation for the theoretical concept of the structure of the atom.

In 1865 Kekulé drew a structure diagram of the benzene molecule. For the first time the idea of a "closed chain" of atomic linkages was proposed. The whole idea of atomic linking was a most fruitful alternative to the ideas of type and substitution; atom linking succeeded in breaking the type-substitution versus dualistic stalemate. Chemists regained their enthusiasm for analysis and were startled to see how easily the most complicated of organic compounds succumbed to their attack. The investigations seemed more challenging in the area of organic compounds, but inorganic substances were also studied. The atom link theory, being found equally suitable for organic and inorganic chemistry, helped show how these hitherto isolated fields were mutually related.

Experimental chemistry was thus spurred on by a breakthrough in theoretical chemistry. Not only were there striking advances in the knowledge of the structure of compounds but there was also a bonus. The study of organic compounds in coal tar led to the tremendous expansion of the color industry and the establishment of manufactures of products derived from coal tar.

Atomic linking was a descriptive technique for explaining the regularity and variety of composition of substances. Chemistry was again on the road to being a descriptive science rather than being engaged merely in classifying a large amount of factual material. The atomic linking theory was no grand scheme, such as Berzelius' dualism, but by making modest advances it was on surer ground.

For those chemists who serenely thought that they had escaped all snares by the introduction of atom linking, there were always uncomfortable reminders of its limitations. Ernst Mach, in his *Popular Scientific Lectures* of the 1880's and 1890's, publicly cautioned against believing that the atom represented "realities behind phenomena." He said that "the atom must remain a tool for representing phenomena, like the functions of mathematics."

In Mach's view, science has an unchangeable character that began with primitive man's first knowledge. A noise in the bush was constructed into an image of the enemy "just as we mentally associate a certain kind of matter with a certain line in the spectrum. . . ." Man continues to form his ideas about the world from "such primitive acts of knowledge," which, Mach said, "constitute today [1882] the solidest foundation of scientific thought." Mach illustrated how this "instinct" or imagination coped with the unperceived. We can accept as usual the way a man "reconstructs the part concealed" when looking at the "visible part of a half-concealed wing of a butterfly." But when a physicist employs the same type of imagination, "we invariably surround their investigations with a metaphysical halo. . . ."

In science an aid to making a whole image is analogy. Mach pointed this out in a lecture given in 1894 titled "On the Principle of Comparison in Physics." A concept, like potential, used in one area acquires "wide-reaching applicability" by use of analogy. "Things as dissimilar as pressure, temperature, and electromotive force now shows points of agreement in relation to ideas derived by definite methods from the concept: viz.," Mach said, "fall of pressure, fall of temperature, fall of potential. . . ."

Mach continually talked about these mental devices in his popular lectures, but he did not lose sight of the fact that they were devices. He referred to molecules and atoms as something that science has "self-created" and that were merely "changeable, economical tools." Mach foresaw that "gradually, however, as the intellect, by contact with its subject matter, grows in discipline, physical science will give up its mosaic play with stones. . .", that is, with atoms. "The goal which it [science] has set itself," Mach emphasized, "is the *simplest* and *most economical* abstract expression of facts."[19]

The atom link theory was a successful adjunct to the atomic theory and it demonstrated the fruitfulness of this approach to chemistry. Theories dealing with the organization of the atoms within a substance was one way of studying matter. The other approach, which dealt more exclusively with the forces in chemical combination, was revived again in the 1870's. In forming a theory of chemical forces, Berthollet had used an analogy with gravity, Berzelius had used electricity, and in 1876 Josiah Willard Gibbs used thermodynamics.

Josiah Willard Gibbs was born in 1839. His father was professor of Sacred Literature in Yale Divinity School. Willard Gibbs' entire life was centered around Yale. He received his bachelor's degree in 1858 and his Ph.D. in 1863, both from Yale. From 1863 to 1866 he was a tutor at Yale in Latin and natural philosophy. His only separation from Yale occurred during the years 1866 to

1869 when he studied abroad. During that period he studied mathematics and physics at Paris, Berlin, and Heidelberg.

Gibbs' studies abroad were predominately in scientific theory and they were in contrast to his training in the United States. His graduate work at Yale was in engineering and his doctoral dissertation was titled "On the Form of the Teeth of Wheels in Spur Gearing." As further evidence of a practical mechanical bent, there are two inventions which he made in his early years. One, an Improved Railway Car Brake, was granted a U.S. patent in 1866.

Gibbs' first three published papers dealt with thermodynamics and are specimens in the evolution of his ideas on that subject. The first paper, "Graphical Methods in the Thermodynamics of Fluids," appeared in *Transactions of the Connecticut Academy* in 1873. Gibbs had a predilection for geometrical illustrations, as his first paper in thermodynamics showed. The paper began with the standard pressure-volume graph then in use in thermodynamics and proceeded to investigate all possible variations of this graph. He developed mathematical and graphical aids known as *isometric, isopiestic, isothermal, isodynamic,* and *isentropic lines* (constant volume, pressure, temperature, energy, and entropy lines). The paper concluded by comparing the state of any body with the position of a point in a plane. Each is capable of two, and only two, independent variations. The diagrams he used were incorporated only to illustrate general theorems. "It is not necessary," Gibbs concluded, "although it may be convenient, to assume any particular method of forming the diagram." That is, no hypotheses as to the causes of or explanations for the state were necessary; "it is enough," he wrote, "to suppose the different states of the body to be represented continuously by points upon a sheet."[20]

The second paper, "A Method of Geometrical Representation of the Thermodynamic Properties of Substances by Means of Surfaces," was a continuation of the first paper. The second paper was published in December 1873, six months after the first and in the same little-known journal, *Transactions of the Connecticut Academy.* The "Surfaces" referred to in the title were constructed by drawing a graph on three axes on which three dimensional curves could be drawn (two axes produced

a flat diagram on a piece of paper). Three basic thermodynamic
quantities, volume, energy, and entropy, could be represented
by a point, above, below, or on a surface.

The idea of a three dimensional diagram for use in thermodynamics was not new. What was new was Gibbs' choice of
the three quantities. The change was more than a modification
of previous work. It was an important innovation which made
the diagram suggestive for further study. The three dimensional
diagram gave an amazing amount of information about the substance being studied. It showed the conditions for equilibrium,
the criteria for stability and instability, the conditions for
coexistent states, and for the critical state. Gibbs illustrated the
usefulness of the diagram for the solution of thermodynamic
problems. If this method could be used for representing a single
substance in different states (solid, liquid, or gas), why not use
the same method to deal with substances differing chemically?
The method promised to be useful for chemistry and this application was something Gibbs had in mind. In the last footnote of
the paper, he wrote that "the body under discussion has been
supposed throughout this paper to be homogeneous in substance," but "any material system" could be used.

Few scientists saw how important Gibbs' work was because it
was so very different in outlook from the papers being published
in the journals and it involved some difficult mathematics. In
addition, it was in such an out-of-the-way journal. Maxwell was
probably the first person to appreciate the import of Gibbs' work.
Maxwell told others, and soon Gibbs was receiving requests for
reprints. Maxwell himself made a plaster cast of the thermodynamic surface that represented the states of water and sent
it to Gibbs. The handmade plaster cast was a great man's
tribute to an original idea.

The third paper, "On the Equilibrium of Heterogeneous Substances," was the culmination of ideas that had been carried
along two stages in the earlier papers. "On the Equilibrium of
Heterogeneous Substances" appeared as two installments in the
Transactions of the Connecticut Academy. The first installment
was in the October 1875 to May 1876 series and the second in
the May 1877 to July 1878. In all, the essay covered 321 pages of
the journal.

Gibbs had taken the view that substances could be dealt with as a thermodynamic system. Any substance can be thought of, in this view, as a material that can be described by determining its temperature, volume, pressure, energy, and entropy. If the system is in equilibrium, that is, not changing in any of these respects, then mathematical equations can be used for solving for all of the quantities that completely describe a thermodynamic state. The equations could be used to determine all the important quantities even when only a few factors were known.

As viewed by Gibbs, a substance was a system that could be analyzed and studied from the outside. One did not have to know what was inside the system or what were the particular activities going on inside. The most general and least misleading way to deal with a substance was to examine the changes it undergoes when subject to the forces of nature. A substance therefore ceases to be an inanimate chunk of matter and becomes, in the new view, a dynamic system subject to change of state, temperature, and energy, and which can be studied under the special conditions of thermodynamic equilibrium.

At the head of the paper, "Heterogeneous Substances," Gibbs placed Clausius' statement of the first two laws of thermodynamics: (1) The energy of the universe is constant; (2) The entropy of the universe tends to a maximum. Taking this as a starting point and picking up the discussion of the equilibrium of chemically homogeneous substances from the first two papers, Gibbs proceeded to show that the conditions for equilibrium are of universal application. His method of arriving at a general solution was to subject the limited case of a homogeneous substance in equilibrium to major factors that might produce variations or exceptions. The first restriction to be removed was that the substance be chemically homogeneous. The laws of thermodynamic equilibrium were found to apply to different kinds of matter in different states, that is, chemically heterogeneous substances. Then he considered in turn the effects of gravity, of strain in solids, of surface tensions between portions of the substance, and finally of electrical forces. Then followed a mathematical description of "the most characteristic and essential laws of chemical equilibrium."

Gibbs made no assumptions as to the composition of matter.

His analysis applied to all substances whether homogeneous or heterogeneous and whether gas, liquid, or solid. The general conditions of substances could be described, Gibbs believed, by application of the laws of thermodynamics. Gibbs used only three factors, volume, energy and entropy, all of which could be determined by external means without reference to internal structure or actions. In his approach Gibbs was running counter to nineteenth century science's standard approach. The major success of nineteenth century science, the atomic theory in chemistry, the conservation of energy, and the electromagnetic theory of light, were developed by imagining, through use of a model, the internal workings of a system as deduced from external evidence. The model may have undergone changes, as in the kinetic theory of gases, or been scrapped, as in the electromagnetic theory, but the fact remains that the model as representing internal workings had been supremely successful.

Models were a marvelous aid to forming a theory; for some scientists they were irreplaceable as an aid to the imagination. But models became embarrassing as further research required their continual modification to suit the newer facts. Sometimes the early assumptions appeared ridiculous in the face of the experimental evidence.

Gibbs had made no model for the "Heterogeneous Substances." He had not found it necessary to make any assumptions about the size, shape, or force between molecules. His was a mathematical abstraction similar to Fourier and Ampère's work. Gibbs did not depend on imagined constitution of substance and his work was therefore universal in its application.

The phase rule, which was developed in the paper "Heterogeneous Substances," has been described as "the strangest and most versatile equation in physics and chemistry."[21] This one rule has had wide application. For example, it has been used to determine the chemical "potential," in electrical terms, for reversible electrolytic cells and has therefore been important in physical chemistry. The phase rule has been found useful in metallurgy for the production of new alloys, as well as in the fields of mineralogy and petrology.

Gibbs' career was twin-peaked. The first height was "On the Equilibrium of Heterogeneous Substances." He attained another high point in scientific achievement with the publication of his book, *Elementary Principles in Statistical Mechanics*. The subtitle had special importance: *Developed with Especial Reference to the Rational Foundation of Thermodynamics*. The book was published in 1902. It appeared then, and still does, to be difficult. That it was not easy to grasp stemmed from the originality and newness of thought it contained. "One of the principal objects of theoretical research in any department of knowledge," Gibbs had once written, "is to find the point of view from which the subject appears in its greatest simplicity."[22] Framing ideas in terms of greatest simplicity, of course, does not mean that they will be easy to understand.

The development of thermodynamics was described by Gibbs as being "empirically determined," that is, the laws of thermodynamics were derived from experimental results and were not deduced from any general theory or principles. From this empirical point of view, heat and mechanical motion were separate things. Assume that each of the immense number of independent mechanical systems of a body did obey the laws of mechanics. One could not be sure what would be the resultant effect of a great number of these systems taken at once. The attempt to prove theoretically that heat and mechanical motion were identical was not successful. Lord Kelvin (William Thomson) had labeled this attempt a failure in a paper, "Nineteenth Century Clouds Over the Dynamical Theory of Heat and Light," given in April, 1900.

The problem, as Gibbs saw it, was that thermodynamics was based on an assumption that inevitably led to inexactness. The laws of thermodynamics were only able to express "the approximate and probable behavior . . . of a great number of particles. . . ." The reason for the grossness, for laws only being "approximate," was that that was the way the molecular systems appeared "to beings who have not the fineness of perception to enable them to appreciate quantities of the order of magnitude of those which relate to single particles, and who cannot repeat their experiments often enough to obtain any but most probable results."[23]

The object of *Statistical Mechanics* as outlined by Gibbs in his preface was to advance the state of theoretical thermodynamics by relating it to mechanics through the statistical approach. Those who, like Kelvin, saw the problems that beset thermodynamics recognized in Gibbs' work an exceptionally useful accomplishment. The problem in thermodynamics, as seen by Gibbs, was very similar to Maxwell's view of the motion of gas molecules.

It was to be expected that Gibbs' effort to achieve a generality in science should be compared with Maxwell's work. Many believed that Gibbs' *Statistical Mechanics* did "for thermodynamics what Maxwell's treatise did for electromagnetism, and we may say (as Poincaré has said of Maxwell) that Gibbs has not sought to give a mechanical explanation of heat, but has limited his task to demonstrating that such an explanation is possible."[24]

Gibbs' chief contributions were the application of thermodynamics to chemistry and the development of statistical mechanics as a foundation for thermodynamics. The source of his success was what he called his different point of view. Can that view be described as more abstract, more general, or more mathematical?

To begin with, even though Gibbs dealt with phenomena of matter, he made no assumptions about the nature of matter. "Certainly, one is building on an insecure foundation," he wrote, "who rests his work on hypotheses concerning the constitution of matter."[25] He does not even use such conceptions as models or illustrations. In this respect, his approach was much different from the British school, which gained fruitful insights by means of the model.

Gibbs' work was a departure in one other way. He sought greater generality by actual transference of ideas and theories from one branch of science to another. He wondered how one might describe the state of a substance by means of thermodynamic terms and relations. The result was the application of thermodynamics to chemical reactions. In the same way, his attempt to obtain more "exact" ideas in thermodynamics provided him with the basis for theories in statistical mechanics. Gibbs did not use analogy and that is a fundamental departure from the way many of his contemporaries were doing science.

The broadening aspect of the study of science, with its delving further into molecular events, revealed the limitations of the older point of view. Gradually, during the nineteenth century, the idea of imponderable matter which could not be studied gave way to the mechanical model. The model was only used to stimulate thought in directions that could be handled by the mathematics of mechanics. In every case, heat, light, and electricity, as the theories became more general, the model was jettisoned because it had reached the limit of its usefulness.

Gibbs' work is interesting and significant for what it tells about the changed position of nineteenth century science. Time after time, the same technique was applied in the forming of theories. The mechanical model and the use of an analogy with another field became the standard approach. What Gibbs did, in effect, was to skip the model building stage and to begin with the general statement of the theory. He also gave up the use of analogy and directly applied the ideas of one science to another.

Gibbs does not mark a revolutionary break with the past. On the contrary he had obviously learned from the experience of the nineteenth century. His different point of view might be thought of as a short cut but no one can work out a short cut until the main route has been mapped out.

The Motion Within Gases

9   Where to begin the history of a scientific theory is a prickly question. Every new hypothesis has strands leading back to vague beginnings. The criteria should be that only those men and developments that directly led to the acceptance of the idea should be counted.

How is it possible to determine at what point hypothesis has been accepted and how to decide which events led directly to the acceptance? Why did scientists in one period decide that some hypotheses were wildly speculative and therefore unfounded, and other hypotheses were reasonable and respectable? Notice how the question of *what* is acceptable shades into the issue of *how* acceptability is determined. Respectability comes from being associated with authority. Preferably the scientist himself has an authority based on past accomplishments. For example, many good (and also bad) ideas that were started by Newton remained current for over 150 years, kept alive by the authority of the name. Another basis of authority is established theories. Here the new hypothesis can gain support if the originator can show that his hypothesis is an extension of one that has been accepted. Therefore, we want to know by what authority a new hypothesis was presented; this is one method, not a foolproof one, of determining the prospects for acceptability of the new idea. New hypotheses must, in addition, be presented in acceptable ways. Scientists set the rules for presentation. The truth or falsity of hypothesis will be argued on whether there is enough experimental or mathematical proof. If the idea has not been presented in a way that can be tested by approved means, it will not have attained the status of being worthy of argument. Countless new hypotheses have been ignored, rather than disproved, because of the method of presentation. This negation by indifference explains the many cases in the history of science in which neglected hypotheses are rediscovered. The man who does the rediscovering accidentally comes upon the idea as being similar to the one that he has proposed. The latecomer then restates the hypothesis in acceptable language and we have another example of a man who proposed the idea first not getting deserved recognition. How many countless people never do become discovered by succeeding generations? The task of doing right by all of these unsung heroes in the history of science is a hopeless task and fruitless.

All that has been said above can be briefly stated. A scientific hypothesis only has chance of success if it is, in concept and in presentation, in agreement with the prevailing philosophy of science. The prevailing philosophy is not enshrined some place, nor was it, all during the nineteenth century, something that scientists were even conscious of, but they did operate on certain principles. "In natural science, as in economics or morals or law, people begin with the details. They begin by tackling individual problems as they arise," R.G. Collingwood has written. "Only when this detail has accumulated to a considerable amount do they reflect upon the work they have been doing and discover that they have been doing it in a methodical way, according to principles of which hitherto they have not been conscious."[1]

By tracing the development of theories during a period we are, in fact, describing the prevailing philosophy of science. In addition, we find in the modification of methods, which comes about "in tackling individual problems as they arise," that the prevailing philosophy has changed. An apt illustration of the history being illuminated by and illuminating the philosophy is the invention of the kinetic theory of gases. In the history of this theory were both kinds of authority, human and ideological.

In 1821 *The Annals of Philosophy* published an article, "A Mathematical Inquiry into the Causes, Laws, and Principal Phaenomena of Heat, Gases, Gravitation, &c." by John Herapath. The article, as can be seen by the title, was a far-ranging one with almost the whole realm of physical science being covered. It contained some suggestions as to the causes of gas pressure. Herapath wrote that the random motion of small, hard, indestructible atoms produced the effects of pressure.

A letter written by Herapath which introduced the article explained that it had originally been written for the *Transactions of the Royal Society* but that the article was withdrawn after a nine month period of "discouraging and extraordinary" conduct on the part of some members in the form of an "illiberal opposition."

John Herapath was one of those colorful and combative men who liven and provoke. They are found in every field of endeavor playing the role of the outsider and critic. They are as necessary to the health of an organization as adrenalin is to the human body. By their very nature they must be outside of the establishment, and their originality usually withers should they become accepted.

John Herapath was born in 1790. His father was a maltster, and the son went into the business after what has been described as a "scanty education." With a restless intellect and an interest in mathematics and physics, he gave up business to open an academy. He occasionally contributed articles to the *Annals of Philosophy*. In 1819 he announced in the *Philosophical Magazine* that he had determined the principle of gravity. The article which was to follow described this discovery, but as we have seen, it was turned down by the Royal Society and was finally published in the *Annals of Philosophy*, which was considered by Herapath as a marked comedown.

Among Herapath's subsequent contributions to the *Annals* was a series of articles listing his grievances against the Royal Society. Again Herapath was in the forefront because his articles attacking the Royal Society appeared in 1822, eight years before the better-known and more effective criticism of Charles Babbage. Herapath also wrote an article for the *Annals*, "Tables of Temperature · and a Mathematical Development of the Causes and Laws of the Phaenomena which have been adduced in support of the hypothesis of Calorific Capacity and Latent Heat." It was based on a wrong idea and it was quickly labeled an error.

We find Herapath also clashing with Lord Brougham, who had so bitterly attacked Thomas Young's wave theory of light. The conflict of firebrands was over a promised treatise to be written by Herapath, and a promised appointment for Herapath at the University of London. Herapath found another major interest in life with the advent of railroads. He became editor and proprietor of a magazine, which became known as *Herapath's Railway and Commerical Journal*. He turned over active management of the magazine to his son and in 1847 published two volumes of a work, *Mathematical Physics* or the *Mathematical Principles of Philosophy: with a Development of the Causes of Heat, Gaseous Elasticity, Gravitation &c.* A projected third volume was never finished.

The *Annals of Philosophy* had provided Herapath with the best rostrum he was ever to have. His ideas were suggestive but not as substantial as he believed. They were in error in many places and they were so far-reaching that it would have taken considerable amount of work to test them. They attempted a tremendous task of revising all of physical science with very little in the way of experiment or calculation for support. Even with the references to Newton, Herapath presented something to the scientific community that had no real claim to authority, since he was contravening Newton in many ways. Finally, the speculations were not presented in an acceptable manner so that the ideas could be tested. Since Herapath had not done enough work, the ideas were only to be considered as interesting speculations. In cases like this, the usual outcome is neglect rather than refutation.

The *Annals* played an important role here at least in giving Herapath a hearing. It was again serving as a sounding board for new and radical theories as it did in the publication of Dalton's speculations on the atomic theory. The Royal Society continued to be a bulwark against radically new ideas. But by the end of the 1820's, it was becoming apparent that the Royal Society had slipped and was no longer representative of the prevailing philosophy of scientists. The correction for such failure was the creation of a new establishment, in this case, The British Association for the Advancement of Science.

One of the reasons we know of Herapath's speculation on the role of hard, massy particles in the characteristics of gases is the reference to him by James Prescott Joule, a man who had had his share of rebuff. In 1848 Joule read a paper before the Manchester Literary and Philosophical Society and published it in the Society's *Memoirs* in 1851. An abstract of the paper also appeared in the BAAS *Report* in 1848. Joule began with some postulates including the one he believed he had helped establish: heat was simply a mechanical effect, not a substance. He also stated that the heat of gases was due to their *vis viva* (kinetic energy). These were two hypotheses, Joule noted, that ventured to describe the way gas particles moved. He was partial to the rotary view posited by Humphry Davy, but "nevertheless, since the hypothesis of Herapath, in which it is assumed that the particles of a gas are constantly flying about in every direction with great velocity, the pressure of the gas being owing to the impact of the particles against any surface presented to them, is somewhat simpler, I shall employ it in the following remarks on the constitution of elastic fluids [gases]; premising, however, that the hypothesis of a rotatory motion accords equally well with the phaenomena."[2]

Joule believed that these assumptions were the clue to the calculation of the specific heat of the different gases. Assuming that the temperature of gases was dependent on the motion of gas particles, Joule saw a way of computing the specific heats by first calculating the velocity of the particles. His results indicated that a hydrogen particle had to be moving 6225 feet per second to produce atmospheric pressure at a temperature of 60 degrees. Dalton revived the atomic theory to account for regularity in chemical combination and Joule found a use for the same particle to account for the temperature of gases. The hypothesis that gases consisted of hard, impenetrable, massy particles was gathering credence from different areas of study. This type of cross-checking of hypotheses gave a new idea the kind of support that was hard to shake.

An article, "On the Nature of the Motion which we call Heat," was reprinted in the *Philosophical Magazine* for August, 1857. It took a new approach to the motion of gas, as can be seen by a statement that read, in part, "there is no doubt that actually the greatest possible variety exists amongst the velocities of the several molecules." The article was first printed in Poggendorff's *Annalen* and was written by Rudolf Clausius.

Clausius was born in Pomerania in 1822. He was the sixth of eighteen children, a family which his father managed to support on the income of a school inspector. The son had a standard education, spending four years at the University of Berlin and migrating to Halle, where he took his degree in 1848. His first appointment was to the Royal Artillery and Engineering School in Berlin as professor of physics, in 1850. He held a succession of positions leading from Zurich to Wurzberg and finally to the University at Bonn in 1869. Clausius' reputation came primarily from his work in thermodynamics. He developed the idea of and coined the word for *entropy,* a concept that is as far reaching as it is difficult to comprehend. Clausius independently worked out the second law of thermodynamics. He shared honors of priority for this work with William Thomson. His particular interest was thermodynamics as applied to the study of vapors and gases. It was in this area of investigation that he began his study in the cause of the effects produced by a gas.

In his 1857 paper, "On the Nature of the Motion which we call Heat," Clausius stated that he had formed "a distinct conception" of the cause of heat. He had even made several "investigations and calculations," all before the publication of his first memoir on heat in 1850. These ideas were not necessary to his discussion of heat so that he "intentionally avoided mentioning this conception, because I wished to separate the conclusions which are deducible from certain general principles from those which presuppose a particular kind of motion. . . ."[3]

Clausius had distinguished between what he believed were solidly based hypotheses, among them his second law of thermodynamics, and the more speculative ideas. He did not want the introduction of speculation to jeopardize acceptance of his other views. While waiting for an opportunity to write of his views on the notion of this motion, Clausius was chagrined to read about some of these views in a published article. He heard that Joule had also anticipated him, but he had not seen Joule's article, which was published in the *Memoirs of the Literary and Philosophical Society of Manchester*. Clausius regretted that Joule had not published his article in a "more widely circulated periodical." It was in response to this footnote that Joule had his article reprinted in the *Philosophical Magazine*. (Joule noted in the introduction to the reprinted article that the *Memoirs of the Literary and Philosophical Society of Manchester* were being regularly forwarded to Europe and America.)

Clausius' approach was distinctively different from any previous papers on the subject in the way he dealt with the motions of the gas particles mathematically. Whereas Joule had calculated the velocity of a single molecule, Clausius dealt with molecules in aggregate. Molecules, he wrote, did not rebound after collision "like two elastic balls" but were subject to other motions. After equilibrium had been reached, he wrote, "we may, in our investigation of the total action of a great number of molecules, neglect the irregularities occurring at the several collisions, and assume that, in reference to the translatory motion, the molecules follow the common laws of elasticity."

Clausius deduced the characteristics of the molecular motion in gases from Mariotte's gas law, which give the relationship between volume and pressure (often referred to as Boyle's Law). Also taking into account the fact that the pressure of a perfect gas varied according to the absolute temperature, Clausius was led to the conclusion that gases·had the following characteristics: (1) the molecules were infinitesimal in comparison to the total space occupied by the gas; (2) the duration of the impact between molecules must be infinitesimal in comparison to the time between impacts; and (3) the influence of the force of molecules on each other must be infinitesimal. "If these conditions are not fulfilled," he wrote, "deviations in several ways from the simple laws of gases necessarily arise. . . ."[4]

Clausius assumed that the gas molecules did not all move at the same velocity. Rather, he assumed that there was a great variety of velocities among them. In order to deal with so many variables, he assigned a mean velocity for all. Then he was able to show mathematically that the resultant impact of all of the molecules against the side of the containing vessel would result in a constant pressure. Many velocities of many molecules produced one pressure.

Clausius had increased the intricacy of the imagined motion of gas molecules. Up till his time, theories had postulated one or another type of motion to account for the action of gases. Joule had assumed one type of motion, movement in a straight line, and one velocity for all the gas molecules, and he had been able to calculate their velocity in order to get a resultant pressure and specific heat. Clausius had taken into account several different gas laws and he found it necessary to assume several types of motion and a great number of different velocities. Joule had dealt with many molecules in motion by simplification. Clausius showed that all the variety of activity within a vessel holding gas could be handled at once. His technique was to think of the gas molecules in the aggregate. He had chosen the concept of the mathematical mean to deal with aggregates. It was an important step in method.

The hypothesis concerning the motion of gas molecules as advanced, with variations, by Joule, Kronig, and Clausius had aroused interest. But for many the relationship between the idea of motion and the standard gas laws was difficult to conceive. More mundane questions were raised. If gas molecules moved in straight lines, one doubter asked, why did tobacco smoke in a room remain in immovable layers, or why did not smoke clouds disappear quickly in open air, or why were not strong odors detected at considerable distances quickly? All of these questions deal with the same problem: if gas molecules move, as was said, in straight lines at velocities of over 6000 feet per second, why was not the diffusion of gases much faster?

Clausius sought in his next paper, which was published in the *Philosophical Magazine* in 1859, to clear up the apparent conflict between his hypothesis and everyday experience. Perhaps he was trying to clarify his own ideas and at the same time, as he said, he hoped to prevent further misunderstanding. The hypothesis of the motion of gas molecules was now at the first level of abstraction. It was originally coined to explain phenomena like specific heat and gas pressure. These are quantities that must be defined and are not a matter of everyday experience. Clausius was pausing, now, to deal with a challenge from the realm of everyday experience.

To elucidate ideas about molecular paths, Clausius decided to illustrate this motion in order to better understand the forces involved. These suggestions, he cautioned, were not essential to the hypothesis "but are merely intended to fix our ideas." What he proposed to do was to provide "special hypotheses" whose "only purpose is to facilitate the comprehension by giving something definite to the imagination."

According to the "special" hypothesis, there were two forces exerted between molecules, attraction and repulsion. Attraction was exerted when molecules were at some distance from each other. It made no difference, Clausius thought, whether repulsion was conceived of as the result of the clash between solid elastic bodies or whether repulsion was imagined as acting over a minute distance. Using these assumptions, Clausius calculated the probability of contact between any two molecules. He introduced the idea of *mean path*. He had assumed that molecules had either very long or very short paths between collisions. Since there was no way of telling about individual molecules, Clausius again made use of the mathematical mean. No one knew how small the molecules themselves were, but according to the chemical and physical experiments, they were extremely small and it followed that the number of molecules in a space, e.g. one liter, was very large. Clausius concluded that the mean path of the molecules was very small. In other words, gas molecules under ordinary conditions may travel very fast, as Joule believed, but they did not travel very far before they collided with another molecule.

Taking these calculations based on a special hypothesis of the high probability of collision between molecules, Clausius applied these results "to the externally recognizable behaviours of a gas." He thought it "easy to convince oneself that the theory which explains the expansive force of gases does not lead to the conclusion that two quantities of gas bounding one another must mix with one another quickly and violently." Very few of the molecules actually manage to travel great distances and therefore smoke would not diffuse rapidly and odor would not move quickly across a room. The results of the calculations of the mean path indicated that the great majority of the molecules "only gradually mix at the surface of their contact."[5]

The difficulty of the new gas hypothesis was, as Clausius and others recognized, in the conception. His efforts to "elucidate" indicated that he knew that a mathematical presentation was not sufficient. Clausius had created some pictures of what the molecular motion might be like, insisting that these illustrations were not necessary to the theory but should be helpful in understanding the hypothesis or in conceiving of it.

James Clerk Maxwell in an address to the Mathematical and Physical Sections of the British Association said that the man of science in his efforts to "acquire and develope clear ideas of things" should employ different forms which appeal to different types of minds. One type of mind "can go on contemplating with satisfaction pure quantities presented to the eye by symbols. . . ." Others "feel more enjoyment in following geometrical forms" and still others "are not content unless they can project their whole physical energies into the scene which they conjure up. They learn at what a rate the planets rush through space, and they experience a delightful feeling of exhilaration. They calculate the forces with which the heavenly bodies pull at one another, and they feel their own muscles straining with the effort."

Not one of these attitudes of mind had an exclusive claim on truth and none should be considered either the only or even the best way of developing ideas. Maxwell favored the presentation of ideas in all of the different forms and truth "should be regarded as equally scientific, whether it appears in the robust form and vivid colouring of a physical illustration, or in the tenuity and paleness of a symbolical expression."[6]

Maxwell was not just sympathetic to the various ways of presenting ideas; he was equally at home with all three methods. As a boy he had made mechanisms for drawing intricate geometrical designs. When at Cambridge University, he earned high distinction in mathematical competition. A prize essay that he wrote on the composition of Saturn's rings was not only brilliant in the mathematics used (according to the estimate of his contemporaries) but the motion of the rings was illustrated with a working mechanical model. His articles on Faraday's lines of force had indicated a facility with physical ideas and, among other things, a familiarity with the steam engine.

Maxwell's first venture into the field of the motion of gases was a paper, "Illustrations of the Dynamical Theory of Gases," which was read in 1859. His object, as stated in his opening sentence, was to be able to deduce some properties of matter, especially gaseous, from the hypothesis that matter consisted of minute parts "in rapid motion." What was, he wanted to know, "the precise nature of this motion. . . ."? Clausius had not been able to determine certain quantities relative to the motion of gas particles, but if the investigation was broadened to include other phenomena, such as internal friction of gases, the conduction of heat through a gas, and the diffusion of one gas through another, the result would be a fuller knowledge of the motion of the particles. Two views about the nature of the particles were possible. One was that gases were made up of small, hard, and perfectly elastic spheres. The other view considered the particles as centers of force, and it was evident to Maxwell that "either assumption will lead to the same results." For simplicity and in "order to lay the foundation of such investigations on strict mechanical principles," Maxwell chose the elastic sphere concept.

Maxwell's method for dealing with many particles moving at a variety of velocities was the mathematical theory known as *the method of least squares*. This enabled him to derive a mathematical expression for the average number of particles that were traveling at a given velocity. His assumption was that the whole group of gas particles within a given volume could be dealt with in the same way that statisticians deal with large populations of people. There is no way of telling who will come down with a cold in a given week, but you can statistically determine how many people out of a given group of people will get colds in a given week. The particles in a given volume of gas may be traveling at velocities anywhere from zero to infinity. By assuming some characteristics, for example, that the mass of each particle was the same and the energy of the whole volume was evenly distributed, then statistical determinations could be made. Maxwell assumed that in a vessel where particles had been colliding for a certain time, the energy would eventually be divided among the particles "according to some regular law." It was then possible to compute the average number of particles whose velocity lay between "ascertainable" limits even "though the velocity of each particle" changed continually and therefore individual velocities could not be determined.

To substantiate his mathematical theory, Maxwell deduced the gas laws dealing with pressure, temperature, and density from his equations. His purpose, as Clausius' had been, was to verify the new theory by showing that it did not conflict with the well-established gas laws. Maxwell's equations yielded the fact, known by chemists, that equal volumes of gases contain equal numbers of particles. He found an explanation for viscosity, or internal friction of gases, for the diffusion of gases, and for the fact that air was a poor conductor of heat. Finally, Maxwell satisfied himself that the hypothesis of spherical particles was in agreement with the calculated specific heat of gases.

Not all of the results were as anticipated. The mathematics seemed to indicate that the coefficient of friction of gases was independent of their density. "Such a consequence of a mathematical theory is very startling," Maxwell admitted, "and the only experiment I have met with on the subject does not seem to confirm it."[7]

Maxwell had presented his ideas in two different forms. The use of the hard elastic balls enabled him to employ the mechanical analogy, which he favored so much in all of his work. It also was what he had called the "robust form and vivid colouring of a physical illustration." At the same time, his introduction of the mathematical theory of probability would appeal to those who liked "the tenuity and paleness of a symbolical expression." That these two ways of looking at the phenomena produced no conflict was confirmation of his hypothesis.

The fundamental hypothesis of Herapath, Clausius, and Maxwell was that gas phenomena were produced by the action of widely separated molecules in motion. Maxwell had extended Clausius' hypothesis by showing that several additional gas laws could be deduced from the fundamental hypothesis. Maxwell had inserted several more links between the accepted truths of the gas laws and the new hypothesis, thereby placing the new hypothesis on a firmer basis. It makes very little difference who originated the idea of molecules in motion in gases because, as Clausius pointed out, all that can be done is to determine who helped "to develope the vague idea into an admissable physical theory."

Clausius followed with an article, "On the Conduction of Heat by Gases," which was translated and published in the *Philosophical Magazine* in 1862. He praised Maxwell's memoir as being "remarkable for the elegance of its mathematical developments." But then Clausius politely demurred at some of the results in Maxwell's work by stating that "nevertheless I do not believe that its contents are correct in every point."

What appeared to be a minor objection points up a major difference in approach. Maxwell had used the rules of probability, Clausius remarked, to deduce "a formula purporting to represent the manner in which the various existing velocities are distributed among the molecules."[8] Clausius was able to use the idea of mean velocities because he had made particular assumptions about gas molecule motion. He therefore believed that the general equations based on Maxwell's use of probability were not necessary for the limited case of gas particles. Of course, it was just this broad generality that made Maxwell's work so widely applicable.

Maxwell had made some errors. He forgot to convert his units from English pounds to kilogrammes and he used hours of time when he obviously meant to use seconds.

Maxwell gave a paper, "On the Dynamical Theory of Gases," in 1866. At the start he announced that he had changed his concept of the molecules of gas from that of elastic spheres to that of very small bodies which repel each other. The reason for the change was the result of some experiments which he had recently conducted and which were reported to the Royal Society in the Bakerian Lecture for 1866. The title of that lecture was "On the Viscosity or Internal Friction of Air and other Gases." The results of these experiments indicated that the viscosity of gases was proportional to the absolute temperature. He felt that this result required him "to adopt the hypothesis of a repulsive force inversely as the fifth power of the distance between the molecules, which is the only law of force which gives the observed result."[9]

Maxwell had formed his concept of the molecule by a combination of experimental evidence and mathematical deduction. He said later that "if the skill of the mathematician has enabled the experimentalist to see that the quantities which he has measured are connected by necessary relations, the discoveries of physics have revealed to the mathematician new forms of quantities which he could never have imagined for himself."[10]

The idea of the molecule had undergone some additional changes. Originally, the gas molecule was a physical concept stemming from the hypothesis that heat was a form of motion. The molecule in this stage was simply an elastic ball that was able to produce pressure by concerted action and whose motions conformed to the gas laws (Mariotte's and Charles'). The molecule took on more intricate characteristics as a result of Clausius' and Maxwell's mathematics. They were able to deduce the relative size of molecules, the length of the mean path, and the number of collisions per second. Then, as a result of his experiments, Maxwell was prepared to give up the idea of elastic balls and adopt the concept of molecules being points of force whose repulsive force had to vary inversely as the fifth power of the distance between them.

The concept of molecules as points of force in space with attractive and repulsive powers was reverting back to the speculative idea of the eighteenth century Russian scientist Roger J. Boscovich. But what was emerging as a result of the mathematicians' and the experimentalists' efforts was not that it was becoming easier to make a choice between one view and the other, but that it was becoming increasingly evident to some that it did not matter which picture of the molecule you adopted. Start with Boscovich's idea of a point force, Maxwell suggested, and assume that they attract each other at certain distances but then begin to repel as the distance between them decreases. The repulsive force rapidly increases as the distance decreases and it becomes enormous when the two molecules are about to touch. Then, Maxwell noted, "the phenomena will be precisely the same as those of smooth elastic spheres."[11]

It will not surprise us to find that Maxwell's work with the theory of gases bears striking similarities to his work in electricity. His use of the word dynamical in both cases shows how much he relied on mechanical analogy. "A Dynamical Theory of the Electromagnetic Field" was read by Maxwell in 1864. This was the culmination of his thinking on electromagnetism. It was highly mathematical and had been shorn of all previous physical concepts, except one. The word dynamical in the title, Maxwell said, came from the assumption that the space surrounding magnetic and electric bodies was filled with matter in motion.

Two years later, in 1866, Maxwell read, "On the Dynamical Theory of Gases." The dynamical in this case came from the assumption that all bodies, even when they appeared to be at rest, consisted of molecules in motion.

The acceptance of Maxwell's dynamical view of electromagnetic action and of gases stems from the fact that his presentation appealed to both schools, the mathematical theorists and the model builders. In both cases he began with what was natural to him, that is, a physically conceived medium. These were the vortices in the case of electromagnetism and solid elastic balls for the gases. Then he deduced the mathematical consequences. of these conceptions, but so general was his mathematical treatment that it did not rely on the physical model for its validity.

The dynamical view was the invention of invisible particles of matter, vortices and molecules, as the agents for transmitting energy such as electricity, light, and heat. These particles, aside from a minuteness that made them imperceptible, obeyed the laws of nature, that is, they behaved like any other particle of matter. The dynamical view was a nineteenth century invention that substituted invisible ponderable matter for the mystical, unnatural imponderables of the eighteenth century.

In his thinking, Maxwell was more the mathematician than the physicist. Faced with the dilemma of a choice between a physical concept, or model, and a mathematical abstraction, Maxwell chose the abstraction. In this tendency he was different from most of his British fellow-scientists, like Faraday or William Thomson. Maxwell saw that the laws of dynamics could be applied to the collision of molecules as long as there were only two molecules involved. But he noted that "the smallest portion of matter which we can subject to experiment consists of millions of molecules, not one of which ever becomes individually sensible to us." The method of dynamics had to be abandoned and the statistical method of dealing with large groups had to be adopted. Something new was thereby added to the scientific outlook by its broadening compass. It was not a matter of sacrificing accuracy or rigor for more speculative ideas. The use of statistics was the *only* way of dealing with the phenomena of molecules in motion. New fields of exploration required new techniques. "In studying the relations between quantities of this kind," Maxwell told a group at the British Association for the Advancement of Science, "we meet with a new kind of regularity, the regularity of averages, which we can depend upon quite sufficiently for all practical purposes, but which can make no claim to that character of absolute precision which belongs to the laws of abstract dynamics.

"Thus molecular science teaches us," he concluded, "that our experiments can never give us anything more than statistical information, and that no law deduced from them can pretend to absolute precision."[12]

Many contributed to the extension and verification of the kinetic theory of gases between 1860 and 1880. Ludwig Boltzmann did much to place the mathematics on firmer ground by making fewer assumptions than Maxwell and using a stricter mathematical proof. But the theory at the end of Boltzmann's work was still only "a very successful and interesting analogy."[13] Much evidence had been heaped up to show the quantitative agreement between the theory and the behavior of gases, but there was still no proof of the existence of atoms and molecules. As a hypothesis the molecular theory of matter found support in the chemical theory of combination and in the kinetic theory of gases. But just because it was reasonable and useful did not "prove" the existence of molecules. Some wanted more specific, less indirect evidence, of their existence.

The advent of atomic physics with the discovery of X-rays in 1895 was firmer support for the kinetic theory. The motions of ions and electrons as postulated in the new field were essentially in agreement with the original concept of the motion of gas molecules. The Brownian movements in liquids and the oil-drop phenomena gave further experimental proof. All of these different means of confirmation have made the·kinetic theory of gases, today, "as well-established a theory (that is, a close working mechanical analogy to the real process) as any theory which is accepted by science."[14]

The belief that the properties of matter can best be explained by the concept of minute, indivisible particles (atoms) is at least as old as Democritus, a Greek of about the fifth century B.C. The idea was periodically revived. Each time there was supporting evidence that bore the characteristics of the philosophy of science of that time, or, as Maxwell said, the language of the theory "must of course be interpreted according to the physical ideas of the age."

What can we tell about the physical ideas of the nineteenth century through the study of the kinetic theory of gases? The fact that the hypothesis was couched in dynamical terms puts it in agreement with an underlying theme of nineteenth century science. One need only review the theories dealing with heat, light, and electricity to see how pervasive the dynamical idea was. When attempting to treat the kinetic theory quantitatively, Clausius and Maxwell found that the only possible mathematics was the mathematics of averages or statistics. This new approach led, as we have seen, to a radical change in outlook which radiated out from gas theory to affect the rest of the areas of science.

Scientific work has a secondary effect, Maxwell wrote; it leaves the investigator "in possession of methods which nothing but scientific work could have led him to invent. . . ." Maxwell had the concept of molecules in mind when he added that the investigator is placed in "a position from which many regions of nature, besides that which he has been studying, appear under a new aspect."[15] Unquestionably, the kinetic theory of gases put a "new aspect" on the view of all matter, making the molecular theory more acceptable in other areas, for example, chemistry.

From one point of view, a view expressed by Sir William Thomson in 1884, the whole kinetic theory sprang from a flimsy mechanical model. Thomson spoke of the theory as a "mechanical model of a gas out of little pieces of round, perfectly elastic solid matter, flying about through the space occupied by the gas, and colliding with one another and against the sides of the containing vessel. This is, in fact, all we have of kinetic theory of gases up to the present time, and this has done for us, in the hands of Clausius and Maxwell, the great things which constitute our first step towards a molecular theory of matter."[16]

Thomson was expressing the prevailing outlook of the period when he said that the flimsy model only became an acceptable explanation when considered in relation to other theories. The interconnections that a hypothesis had with other hypotheses produced a stronger structure for all. "All the properties of matter are so connected that we can scarcely imagine one *thoroughly explained*," Thomson said, "without our seeing its relation to all the others, without in fact having the explanation of all. . . ." Such completeness was an unobtainable goal, but scientists were at least moving towards that goal, he believed, "on many different roads converging towards it from all sides. The kinetic theory of gases is . . . a true step on one of the roads."[17]

An important effect on the philosophy of science by the kinetic theory of gases was a modification of the definition of explanation. Maxwell in his paper, "On the Dynamical Evidence of the Molecular Constitution of Bodies," spoke of explanations as being "of very various orders, according to the degree of generality of the principle which is made use of." An explanation of the highest order can be said to exist "when a physical phenomenon can be completely described as a change in the configuration and motion of a material system, the dynamical explanation of that phenomenon is said to be complete." The nineteenth century scientists accepted an explanation as being complete when it was reduced to the simplest elements of nature known: configuration, motion, mass, and force. "We cannot conceive any further explanation to be either necessary, desirable, or possible, for as soon as we know what is meant by the words, configuration, motion, mass and force," Maxwell said, "we see that the ideas which they represent are so elementary that they cannot be explained by means of anything else."[18]

An explanation, in order to be satisfactory, did not have to represent absolute and complete truth. Maxwell, more than any other single person, helped to shape the prevailing opinion. When he spoke of not being able to conceive of any further explanation as being "necessary," "desirable," and "possible," he was expressing the philosophical outlook that had resulted from the changes wrought in and by nineteenth century science. The statistical method and the dynamical explanation were characteristic of nineteenth century science. They were the result of the accumulation of details in the various branches of science. Towards the end of the century, philosophers of science and men of science took time to "reflect upon the work" they had been doing and they discovered that they had been working, as Collingwood said, "in a methodical way, according to principles of which hitherto they have not been conscious."

Cathode Rays and Electrons

10   When electricity is discharged in an evacuated glass tube, it produces a fascinating display of colored lights. Experimenters in the eighteenth century were attracted to this phenomena, which some described as similar to the *aurora borealis*. When does a curiosity require an explanation? When it ceases to be a freak occurrence and has some regularity, and especially if it can be produced at will by laboratory equipment.

The more discerning eighteenth century experimenters saw that there was a close relationship between the production of colored lights *in vacuo* and the production of (static) electricity. Francis Hauksbee, in 1709, attributed the lights to electricity and compared it with lightning. William Watson, around 1750, suggested that the lights were electricity seen "without any preternatural force, pushing itself on through the vacuum by its own elasticity. . . ." The Abbé Jean-Antoine Nollet, writing in 1749, saw the phenomena as confirmation of his theory of electricity. He believed that the lights were caused by the collision of the two types of electric matter.[1]

These were the dominant eighteenth century views of the curious phenomena. The pretty lights *in vacuo* were another manifestation of the imponderable electric fluid; here was something else that the strange fluid, electricity, could do. What scientists were collecting was more evidence of what the imponderable was like. They did not seek its essence because it was imperceptible. They collected data on the many and unrelated effects that the imponderable could produce.

A different type of hypothesis was used to explain the lights of the evacuated tube by Julius Plücker, a nineteenth century mathematician and physicist. Plücker's background was a peculiar mixture of the mathematical and physical. He was born in 1801. He received his education while in residence at the universities of Bonn, Heidelberg, and Berlin. This migratory habit was typical of students in Germany. In 1823 he went to Paris, which for him was not only a migration across national boundaries but also a crossing of an intellectual boundary. In Paris, Plücker was influenced by the great school of French geometers, the like of which he could not have found anywhere in Germany.

Plücker started in academic life as professor extraordinary at Bonn. Next he went to a *Gymnasium* in Berlin, where he stayed for one year, at the end of which he went to Halle as professor of mathematics. That was in 1834. Plücker's area of special interest was geometry, which he wanted to establish on an independent and sound basis by combining purely geometrical and algebraic methods. His first work was on the development of analytical geometry and was published in 1828 and 1831. He published a more complete description of his system of analytical geometry in 1835 while at Halle. In 1836 Plücker returned to Bonn as ordinary professor of mathematics, and while there he published a continuation of his mathematical work on the theory of algebraic curves.

What is unique about Plücker's career is that it was broken into distinct parts. He began as a mathematician, and until about 1846 he devoted himself to research and publication in mathematics. But then in 1847 he was appointed professor of physics at Bonn and he began a completely separate career, which was to bring him recognition from a different scholarly community. Plücker's first work in physics bore the imprint of his geometrical orientation. This work was on the magnetic action of crystals. He then became interested in magnetic and diamagnetic bodies. In this work, he was said to be the equal of Faraday.

In 1858 Plücker published his first paper on the effects of magnetism on the electric discharge in an evacuated tube. These researches were the result of a lucky confluence of talents. Heinrich Geissler, the experimental physicist, was at Bonn the same time as Plücker. Geissler had improved the vacuum pump so that it produced vacuums of extraordinary high quality. There is no perfect vacuum, but the degree with which a perfect vacuum is approached makes a marked difference in the use of the vacuum as an experimental tool. Geissler provided Plücker with some evacuated tubes containing two platinum electrodes for performing experiments on electrical discharges through rarefied gases. Even though Geissler was not the first to make this type of tube, the high degree of vacuum achieved by him provided Plücker with a laboratory instrument for examining phenomena never before seen by experimenters.

Plücker did not stop with the mere recording of the colors of "incomparable beauty." The colored lights in the tubes, Plücker maintained, were due to the traces of gas remaining in the tubes; no discharge would occur through an absolute vacuum. Since the colors of the lights depended on the kind of gas in the tube, he saw the spectra as a new method of analyzing gases. Thus, chemical analysis was "the most important part of the subject" to Plücker.[2]

He was a careful and thorough experimenter. As a next step, he wrote, "what was more natural than the thought of approximating such tubes in various ways to the poles of a magnet during the discharge?" Of course, this step appeared natural to someone like Plücker, whose previous experience had been in magnetic theory. Plücker declared that he was only repeating the experiments that Humphry Davy had performed on electric arc discharges in air. In performing what he considered duplicate experiments, Plücker found some expected results and "certain unexpected ones." What was unexpected was the break up of the light near the negative electrode. This striated light looked like magnetic curves, he thought.

Plücker believed it was "premature to attempt to explain fully the stratification of the light produced by the electric discharge, for such might perhaps embrace the explanation of the physical process which takes place on such discharge." Plücker rejected the eighteenth century view that the lights were electricity made visible. Close examination showed "that the discharges of light take place at intervals," which was further evidence for him that the effect was not a stream of imponderable substance. Here was the beginning of a fresh look at the phenomena.

Plücker found it significant that the color of the lights was independent of the material used in the electrodes that were placed at either end of the tubes. But the colors did depend on the gas present in the tube. The lights were an effect of electricity, not electricity itself. The phenomena, Plücker thought, must consist of an aggregation of matter in the tube which became luminous by action of the electric discharge.

The color of the lights was due to the kind of gas in the tube. The light spread out from the negative electrode in lines that resembled, Plücker thought, magnetic curves or lines of force. The light rays assumed the shape that iron-filings assumed when spread in a magnetic field. Plücker concluded that "every ray which is bent in this magnetic curve . . . behaves as a magnetic thread of perfect suppleness . . . or, what comes to the same thing, as an electrical current twisted in an infinitely thin spiral." That was what it was like, but what did the light consist of? What was its nature? Plücker was not prepared to go any further with the evidence he had. "By the above illustrations I have merely sought to make the nature of the phenomenon intelligible," he wrote, "without in the least attempting to describe the nature of the magnetic light itself."[3]

The research and attitude towards the phenomena of the electric discharge in an evacuated tube was set in a direction of a man who was fortunate enough to be the first to use the much improved equipment. The discoveries he had made added weight to Plücker's theory. The ideas were British-like in the particular physical concept used. His reference to the thin spiral of electric current indicated that he was influenced by Ampère. Why should Plücker, who was German in background and education and strongly influenced by the French school of mathematicians, take an attitude so unlike the Continental view? We are told that Plücker was self-taught in the field of physics and that he was imperfectly acquainted with the works of others, for example Gauss and Weber, in the field of electricity and magnetism. The lack of influence here would emphasize the amount of influence Michael Faraday had on him. Plücker was friendly with Faraday and exchanged views with him on their mutual interest, magnetism. It is no wonder that we find Plücker using terms like magnetic lines and also that his work should be more appreciated by the British than by his countrymen. He spoke in terms that were clear to the British but obscure to the French and German.

For two decades, work on the electric discharge followed the lines begun by Plücker. His student Johann W. Hittorf arrived at the conclusion that the cathode was emitting "rays of glow" that followed "rectilinear paths." An analogy with light was clearly indicated.

In 1878 William Crookes began a series of experiments on the luminous phenomena in rarefied gases, which he reported to the Royal Society and to the British Association for the Advancement of Science. Crookes had come to this new field as a chemist. His reputation was gained from the discovery of the element thallium in 1861. He became a Fellow of the Royal Society in 1863.

Crookes had an excellent start in chemistry at the Royal College of Chemistry, London, which he entered at the age of fifteen. Between 1850 and 1854 he was Wilhelm von Hofmann's assistant at the college, but upon finishing his studies, he was unable to find a job in chemistry. He had difficulty in spite of the fact that he had already published some original research on compounds of selenium. Crookes' first job was in a meteorological laboratory and from there he went to a position as lecturer in chemistry at a training college.

He married in 1856 and moved to London, where he founded *Chemical News,* a journal with an informal format unlike any of the scientific journals of the day. It was a financial success and Crookes was able to support himself and family in addition to maintaining a private laboratory. He had become a journalist, consultant, and some-time teacher of chemistry.

What had brought Crookes to the study of the electric discharge was his work on thallium. In those researches he used a vacuum balance. He was fortunate, as he declared, in having a friend and assistant, named C. H. Gimingham, "whose dexterity in executing complicated forms of apparatus has rendered easy a research which otherwise would have been full of difficulties." Great technical skill was essential to this new field, where a very high vacuum was required and where considerable dexterity was employed in placing finely constructed metalwork in the tubes.

Crookes' first paper on the electric discharge was delivered before the Royal Society in 1878. The paper was titled "On the Illumination of Lines of Molecular Pressure, and the Trajectory of Molecules." Crookes had observed, he reported, the shadow of the negative electrode on the tube wall. He then constructed targets which he placed between the electrode and the tube wall. In every case, the shadow of the target was projected on the glass. These shadows were, he claimed, the result of "the direct impact of the molecules on the surface of the glass." Had the cause been "optical," the shadows would not have been as sharply defined.

Crookes also said that he had produced mechanical motion inside an evacuated tube by means of the molecular motions. He had introduced into the tube a radiometer, which consisted of mica vanes 8 millimeters by 2 millimeters, and this was delicately balanced by a needle point in a glass cup. The paddle wheel was driven, Crookes said, by a molecular stream.

A third occurrence worthy of note, Crookes thought, was the heating effect of the "molecular bombardment," and by concentrating the impacts at one point, the heat might be "rendered apparent." A polished aluminum cup was used to focus the stream of molecules on one point of a properly exhausted glass tube. "To ascertain if heat were developed here I touched it with my finger," Crookes reported, "and immediately raised a blister."

Near the end of his paper, which was a report on a series of successful and interesting experiments, Crookes tentatively rendered "some theoretical speculations which have gradually formed in my mind during the progress of these experiments." They were put forward "only as working hypotheses, useful, perhaps necessary, in the first dawn of new knowledge. . . ."

Crookes' starting point for his hypothesis was the kinetic theory of gases, which assumed that matter in a gaseous state in a very small volume contains, he said, "millions and millions" of molecules having "millions of encounters" per second. What happened when this space was evacuated to a state of near vacuum? Then collisions between molecules become rare, "in which case the average molecule is allowed to obey its own motions or laws without interference. . . ." Three states of matter were known hitherto: they were the solid, liquid, and gaseous, but there was a new, a fourth, state, Crookes maintained, the "ultragaseous or molecular state."

With this ultragaseous or molecular state came a new analogy. The billiard ball analogy of the kinetic theory of gases was not applicable. Crookes compared the free molecules to cannon balls. The "trajectory" of the molecules would depend on the explosive charge or the intensity of the electrical excitation. The curve of the trajectory would depend on the medium through which it passed and the effect of any outside interference. This interference could be a magnetic field, which would be analogous to the gravitational field that operated on cannon balls. "The parallelism is still closer," Crookes noted, "if we compare the evolution of light seen when the shot strikes the target, with the phosphorescence produced in the glass screen by molecular impacts."[4]

Eugen Goldstein, a German physicist, published an article, "On the Electric Discharge in Rarefied Gases," which presented what was to become the German view in the controversy over the nature of the electric discharge. Goldstein's paper appeared in the *Philosophical Magazine* in 1860.

The *Philosophical Magazine,* or as it was known in the mid-nineteenth century, *The London, Edinburgh, and Dublin Philosophical Magazine and Journal of Science,* played a particularly important part in the exchange of views and arguments as physicists on both sides of the Channel tried to make something of the electric discharge phenomena. Foreign papers were translated and published within a few months so that Plücker's and Goldstein's ideas were available to the British scientists shortly after they appeared in Germany. Goldstein mentioned Crookes' article, which he had read in the *Philosophical Magazine* of January, 1879. What Goldstein had read was a full report of the paper that Crookes had given before the Royal Society on December 5, 1878. The *Philosophical Magazine* served during this period as a means of international communication as well as an inter-scientific journal. It published the Proceedings of the Geological Society as well as those of the Royal Society.

In publishing these articles, the *Philosophical Magazine* was fulfilling an established policy of being broadly based, although not as broadly based as the title page of the first issue in 1798 indicated. That page read: *The Philosophical Magazine comprehending the Various Branches of Science, the Liberal and Fine Arts, Agriculture, Manufactures, and Commerce.* But in the nineteenth century the magazine tended much more toward reporting the results of scientific research. It absorbed *Nicholson's Journal of Natural Philosophy, Chemistry and the Arts* and the scientific journal founded by Thomas Thomson known as *Thomson's Annals.*

The *Philosophical Magazine's* ability to select worthwhile articles was not unerring. But it had a high ratio of significant material compared to the nonsensical and not-worth-the-time articles often found in other magazines. This success was all the more noteworthy because it was incautious enough to print controversial ideas. Coverage of the electric discharge controversy was only one of the services provided to the scientific community. The magazine provided a forum for Henry A. Rowland's first scientific paper. Rowland, who was to become one of the best-known American physicists in the nineteenth century, could not find a willing American journal for his first work. He sent the paper to Clerk Maxwell who had it published in the *Philosophical Magazine.* The Michelson-Morley experiment was first published in it in 1887. William R. Hamilton, William Thomson, J.J. Thomson, and many others contributed to the *Philosophical Magazine,* which gave them the international public they deserved and in turn their work published there gave the magazine its special lustre.

The aforementioned article by Goldstein, "On the Electric Discharge in Rarefied Gases," spoke of the "light from the negative pole" of the glass tubes, which he called *cathode-light.* He also made reference to rays that were emitted from the negative pole or cathode. It was he who coined the word

Kathodenstrahlen, or cathode rays, and this was the term that was to be used henceforth in discussing the phenomena of an electric discharge through rarefied gas. Surprisingly, the British accepted the term even though they rejected the idea it implied.

Goldstein showed that a careful analysis of the illumination effects in the cathode tubes revealed several contradictions in Crookes' hypothesis. He pointed out that the cathode light occurred in straight lines, but if Crookes was right the molecules being driven by a repulsive force from the cathode should follow a hyperbolic curve, not a straight line. Goldstein suggested that the cathode rays were transverse vibrations or waves in the ether. In this way, the cathode rays were like light rays as envisaged in the wave theory of light.

Thus, the differences in explanation of cathode rays were drawn along national lines. The British supported Crookes' view, which was founded on the kinetic theory of gases and generally fit what was called the dynamical view of nature. The dynamical view was that physical phenomena resulted from the action of particles impelled by forces. The Germans almost unanimously supported Goldstein's view, which stemmed from the wave theory of light and used the idea of vibrations in the ether. "It would seem at first sight that it ought not to be difficult to discriminate between views so different," J. J. Thomson wrote years later, "yet experience shows that this is not the case, as amongst the physicists who have most deeply studied the subject can be found supporters of either theory."[5]

There was more involved in this controversy than simply deciding who had interpreted the data correctly. Each of the theories had its flaws. The problem for each side was, supposing that our theory is for the most part correct, how do we proceed now? What should be the next step in establishing the theory? Again, as in previous controversies, there was a corollary controversy as to what constituted a satisfactory theory.

Many scientists felt that a theory should "explain" the facts, that is, put the facts into some sort of understandable order. To some scientists a theory was not a law of nature but a mental construct by which man understood nature. One nineteenth century scientist, Joseph Larmor, thought of theories this way: "The uniformities which it is customary to call laws of nature are often just as much laws of mind: they form an expression of the implications between mind and matter, by means of which material phenomena are mentally grasped."[6]

But what constitutes a satisfactory explanation, as was shown in the cathode ray dispute, was based on a scientist's predilection or his philosophy of science. That was exactly what Pierre Duhem, a nineteenth century philosopher of science, wanted scientists to avoid: philosophical disputes. He would therefore define theory more narrowly. "A physical theory is not an explanation," he said. "It is a system of mathematical propositions, deduced from a small number of principles, which aim to represent as simply, as completely, and as exactly as possible a set of experimental laws."

According to Duhem, the use of theory as explanation was a handicap to science since this approach ultimately involved the scientists in insoluble metaphysical questions. To avoid the confusion that would result from a reliance on the personal preference of scientists, Duhem suggested using mathematics as the only means of constructing theories. What was to be the test to determine truth? Duhem claimed that *agreement with experiment is the sole criterion of truth for a physical theory.*"[7] No one disagreed with Duhem on this point but no one seemed to know how to proceed. Regardless of what Duhem thought and notwithstanding all scientists' high regard for the value of experiment, the method in practice in the nineteenth century was one which proceeded from explanation to mathematical propositions.

The cathode ray controversy is an illustration of the nineteenth century method of science in operation. There had been experiments with attempts to explain the phenomena. For example, Plücker's use of magnetic lines, Goldstein's reference to similarity to light, and Crookes' use of the concept of particle. All of these were exploratory experiments whose object was to find an explanation. They obviously were not the type of experiment that Duhem had in mind because, rather than be a test of truth, these experiments had resulted in a division of opinion. Division of opinion as to the correct explanation of phenomena was common enough in nineteenth century science to be the rule. Recall the chemists' differences over constant proportions, the dispute over the nature of heat and the nature of light, and the action of electricity across space.

The experimental test in the case of the cathode rays, as in the other instances, had to be quantitative. Plücker, Goldstein, and Crookes had performed qualitative experiments in order to explain the rays. The explanation had been narrowed to two possibilities, the rays were either waves or particles. Anyone who wanted to put the theory in mathematical terms first had to make a choice between the explanations. If he subscribed to the wave theory, his quantities would be in terms of wave length and frequency; but if he was a particle proponent, his quantities would be such things as mass and charge.

There is another question which can be raised at this point and that is why this particular controversy, over cathode rays, should follow national lines. The difference lay in the way science was organized in the two countries. In Germany, science was university oriented, which meant that it would tend, in those universities particularly, to be influenced by the philosophical or metaphysical and therefore be more at home with an abstraction like ether waves. The influence of French mathematics played an important role too. British scientists, the original thinkers of the earlier years of the century, like Dalton, Faraday, and Joule, were self-taught, weak in mathematics, and strongly influenced by the industrial society in which they lived. Their natural bent was to develop theories by use of physical imagination. They would prefer particles over ether waves.

In the later years of the century, the division between the two countries was not as marked. The Germans were going through a rapid period of industrialization, especially in the manufacture of steel and chemicals. The change influenced the university training by moving it from the metaphysical towards the physical, which was assumed to be the more practical training for those who would devise the new technology. The British, on the other hand, were revamping their university system in order to undertake the training of scientists. In places like Cambridge's Cavendish Laboratory, the new scientists were to be trained and the new scientific theory was to be framed.

Not only were there the two schools of thought on cathode

rays, German and British, but there was disagreement within the schools. Heinrich Hertz's work on cathode rays lent support to the German ether view, but he dissented from this view in important ways. Hertz, primarily an experimentalist, made important contributions to two different fields.

Heinrich Hertz was born in 1857 in Hamburg. He was the son of a lawyer who was active in politics. Hertz's first choice of career was engineering. After a year as an engineering apprentice and six months at a technical high school, he decided to change to the study of pure science. He studied mechanics and mathematics at Munich and at the age of twenty-one transferred to the University of Berlin. That this amount of indecision was unusual and was giving him considerable pain can be seen from the letters he wrote to his parents.

At Berlin he studied with Helmholtz and Kirchhoff, and was soon doing independent and original research. He won first prize in a contest which required solving an experimental problem set by the faculty. Hertz received his doctorate, *magna cum laude*, in 1880, and remained a few years in Berlin to work as Helmholtz's assistant. In 1883 he became lecturer at the University of Kiel, and it was there that he did his first research on cathode rays. He became professor of physics at the *Technische Hochschule* of Karlsruhe, and it was here that he conducted the experiments on electric waves that were to make him famous.

Electromagnetic theory was also a controversial question in 1885. Some scientists, primarily from Britain, adopted an explanation of electromagnetic phenomena that imagined a medium for carrying the energy away from an electric wire. The French took the view that the action between wires consisted of action-at-a-distance, that the idea of a medium was silly and unnecessary. Frenchmen like Ampère had worked out the mathematical consequences of their view. In 1864 Maxwell had succeeded in putting Faraday's physical explanation into mathematical form and had deduced results from his mathematics. For two decades the controversy stood at that juncture: there were two opposing physical explanations and different mathematical propositions deduced from them. The true test now was, as Duhem said, a quantitative experiment, but no one could devise an experiment that would decide the issue.

Hertz, in 1887, designed a means of propagating electromagnetic energy in the form of electric waves and he was able to show that the waves took time to travel from the transmitter to the receiver. Therefore, in the interim they had to exist in a medium. He also showed that the waves could be reflected and refracted in a similar manner to light. These experiments made Hertz famous and proved to most, but not all, scientists that Maxwell's theory was correct.

Hertz's "Experiments on the Cathode Discharge" was published in *Wiedemann's Annalen* for 1883. He reported that he had traced the path of the cathode rays visually and that he used a small magnet to plot the electric current path in the tube. The path of the cathode rays did not coincide with the current path and he concluded "that the cathode rays have nothing in common with the path of the current." Hertz was prepared to accept Goldstein's interpretation of the cathode rays but with an important modification. Hertz agreed that the colored lights in the tube were due to an "ether-disturbance," but he did not think that this disturbance was the work of the cathode. The cathode (negative electrode) emitted a current that produced the cathode rays and these in turn produced the colored light. His assumption was that "the luminescence of the gas in the glow discharge is not a direct effect of the current, but arises indirectly through an absorption of the cathode rays which are produced by the current."

One can see that there were numerous possibilities for explaining the cathode rays by means of physical theories. Hertz chose the ether theory and by means of ingenious experiments he had demonstrated that the cathode rays and the electric current in the tubes were two different things. Hertz was a competent experimenter and no one was able to deny the results of his experiments; those who disagreed could only differ over the interpretation of the results.

As another part of his investigation, Hertz found that the cathode rays exhibited either no reaction or a very feeble one to both electrostatic and electromagnetic forces. The cathode rays were not themselves, Hertz concluded, an electrical phenomena but they were caused by electricity. We can see, then, the picture he had constructed with which to explain the cathode ray phenomena: the cathode rays, he said, "have no closer relation to electricity than has the light produced by an electric lamp."[8]

Hertz's results were not going to win any adherents on the western side of the Channel. To British scientists, Hertz's results were a challenge. On the other hand, a letter to Hertz posted from Berlin said: "I have read with the greatest interest your investigation on the cathode discharge, and cannot refrain from writing to say Bravo!" The letter was signed: H. Helmholtz.[9]

According to Crookes' view, the cathode ray phenomena was produced by negatively charged molecules which were propelled away from the cathode and across the tube. Hertz had shown that the rays were "electrically indifferent." He returned to the topic nine years later in 1892 to deal another blow to the particle theory. The question he now raised was one of transparency. For if cathode rays were analogous to light in so many ways, how to account for their chief difference which was "in respect of their power of passing through solid bodies." He found that substances that were most transparent to light offered "an insuperable resistance to the passage of cathode rays." Hertz was successful in demonstrating that some things were transparent to the rays, but his results were surprising because he found "that metals, which are opaque to light, are slightly transparent to cathode rays."[10]

Here now was a considerable obstacle to those who adhered to the particle theory of cathode rays. British scientists had to admit, as J.J. Thomson said, that "the discovery made by Hertz that the cathode rays could penetrate thin gold-leaf or aluminum was difficult to reconcile with" the particle theory of Crookes.[11]

Joseph John Thomson was born in 1856 near Manchester. His father was a publisher and bookseller. When he was fourteen, it was decided that his career would be engineering and he was placed on the waiting list for apprenticeship to an engineering firm. His father was told that it would be useful if the boy enrolled in Owens College while he was waiting for his apprenticeship to begin. The decision had a most fortunate effect on a young boy with Thomson's talents. At Owens (later Manchester University) Thomson found an illustrious faculty in a broad area of subjects which included not only mathematics, chemistry, engineering, and natural history (botany, zoology, and geology) but also outstanding men in logic and political economy, history and law. The mathematics professor had been a senior wrangler at Cambridge and he was a Fellow of Trinity College. It was he who encouraged Thomson to enter Cambridge in order to study mathematics and physics.

Thomson did not take a degree at Owens but he did receive a certificate and prize in engineering. He entered Trinity College, Cambridge, in 1876 and took his degree in 1880. He was second wrangler in the mathematical tripos and he was second Smith's prizeman. First place in these competitions went to men with high proficiency in mathematics but not necessarily to the most original thinkers. We need only recall the experience of William Thomson and James Clerk Maxwell, neither of whom took first place in the tripos. J.J. Thomson won the Adams prize essay for 1883, for which the subject was vortex rings. The Adams prize was for an original essay in science.

The rest of Thomson's career was centered around Cambridge. In 1880 he became a Fellow of Trinity; two years later he was made a lecturer in mathematics at Trinity and in 1883 became university lecturer in mathematics. The appointment at the age of twenty-eight to be Cavendish Professor of Experimental Physics in Cambridge was the great opportunity in Thomson's scientific career. He maintained the lustre of the position that had been given to it by his predecessors, Maxwell and Rayleigh. While Cavendish Professor, Thomson published his work on the cathode rays. The ferment that he produced there for the study of physics carried seven of his students on to Nobel Prizes. (Thomson won the Nobel Prize in 1906).

Thomson's appointment to the Cavendish Professorship had come as a surprise to many and a great disappointment to several others who considered themselves in line for the position. It was no secret that William Thomson had been approached first to take the position. This was the third time he had been asked and the third time that he decided to remain in Glasgow. There were several other men who had more experience in experimental physics than J. J. Thomson. The appointment came as a surprise to him also, but as it turned out, youthfulness and enthusiasm were what the laboratory needed.

Immediately after assuming the Cavendish Professorship in 1885, Thomson took up the study of the passage of electricity through rarefied gases. He said that he "wished to test the view that the passage of electricity through gases might be analogous to that through liquids, where the electricity is carried by charged particles called ions."[12] Heretofore, the study of cathode rays had used analogies with magetism, the kinetic theory of gases, and the wave theory of light. The conduction of electricity through liquids suggested the idea of negatively and positively charged particles.

In a short paper, "On the Velocity of the Cathode-Rays," which appeared in the *Philosophical Magazine* for 1894, Thomson took steps to test the correctness of the Crookes particle hypothesis as against the Hertz aetherial wave view. The experiments that he performed were to measure the velocity of the cathode rays in order to "enable us to discriminate between the two views held as to the nature of the cathode-rays."[13]

If the velocity of the cathode rays was close to that of light, the result would support the German view; but if the velocity was much smaller than light, the result would support the molecular stream hypothesis. The velocity of the rays was found to be 1,500 less than that of light. The findings were not conclusive. The result was that the ether wave theory proponents now had a stumbling block as formidable as Hertz had put in the way of the particle theorists when he showed that cathode rays penetrated some metals.

In 1895, Jean Perrin, a Frenchman, conducted experiments that seemed to give proof that the cathode rays consisted of negative particles. He constructed a cathode tube that had a shielded cylinder at the end opposite the cathode. An opening in the cylinder towards the cathode admitted the cathode rays. An electroscope connected to the cylinder indicated a negative charge when the tube was in operation. The conclusion that Perrin arrived at was that the cathode rays carried a negative charge. But that was not the same, opponents said, as proving that the cathode rays themselves were particles. The wave theory supporters did not deny that electrified particles were shot off from the cathode; they denied, Thomson said, that "these charged particles have any more to do with the cathode rays than a rifle-ball has with the flash when a rifle is fired."

To show that the luminescence in the tube and the negative charge on the electroscope were different effects produced by a single cause, J. J. Thomson devised a group of experiments which he reported on in 1897. The tube he designed was so constructed that the cathode rays would have to bend before they could enter the collector cylinder. Thomson found that when he bent the cathode rays by means of a magnet, he obtained, at the same time, a negative charge as indicated by the electroscope. (The luminescence on the tube wall indicated the path of the cathode rays themselves.) "Thus this experiment shows," Thomson claimed, "that however we twist and deflect the cathode rays by magnetic forces, the negative electrification follows the same path as the rays." It could no longer be denied, therefore, that "this negative electrification is indissolubly connected with the cathode rays."

The sophistication of Thomson's experiments was an outcome of the cathode ray controversy. Both sides had had enough experience in the construction of plausible arguments to have sharpened their approach to their theories. That is, the rightness and wrongness of each viewpoint had been tested by so many different experiments that everyone was beginning to see more clearly what were the minimum or sufficient requirements for a satisfactory explanation.

The significance of Thomson's experiment was as much a reflection of the progress in cathode ray theory as it was of Thomson's ingenuity. Ten years earlier his experiments would not have had the impact that they did in 1897. Previous experiments had cleared the way by dealing with and estimating the significance of the colored lights (which were accepted as the immediate effect of the rays), the electrical and mechanical effects of the rays, and the relationship between cathode rays and light. The time had arrived, some believed, for an *experimentum crucis* and they were certain, on looking at the evidence, that Thomson had succeeded.

In the first part of his report, Thomson also dealt with the question of electrostatic deflection. If the cathode rays were negative particles, they should be attracted by a positive, and repelled by a negative, electrostatic field, yet Hertz had not been able to produce an electrostatic deflection. Thomson at first got the same result as Hertz. Here we find conviction, overwhelming experimental evidence. All experimental work must be interpreted to find its meaning, as Thomson well knew. He was taking the position of one who finds experimental evidence not as proof of an opposing theory but as an obstacle to one's own belief.

Thomson knew from Röntgen's discovery and experiments with X-rays in 1895, that these rays made gases highly conductive. Upon following up on this idea, Thomson found that the conductivity of the tube decreased rapidly with increased exhaustion of the tube. He wrote that "it seemed then that on trying Hertz's experiment at very high exhaustions there might be a chance of detecting the deflexion of the cathode rays by an electrostatic force." And such was the case. At high degrees of vacuum, a mere two volts of electrostatic charge produced a deflection of the cathode rays.

The first stage of these 1897 experiments had come out completely satisfactory. He found that the cathode rays carried a negative charge, were deflected by an electrostatic field, and were acted on by a magnetic field, all of these results being those that would be expected if a negatively electrified body were moving along the path of the cathode rays. "I can see no escape from the conclusion," Thomson said, "that they [the rays] are charges of negative electricity carried by particles of matter." The very next sentence reads: "What are these particles? are they atoms, or molecules, or matter in a still finer state of subdivision?"

Thomson was convinced of the rightness of his results but so had Crookes been. Many had been convinced, before 1897, of the particle theory of the cathode rays but no one had been able to make the next step to mathematical analysis. For this type of analysis the particle theory had a great advantage, as Thomson pointed out, "since it is definite and its consequences can be predicted." Mathematically, the opposing theory was unmanageable, or so Thomson thought, because "with the aetherial theory it is impossible to predict what will happen under any given circumstances, as on this theory we are dealing with hitherto unobserved phenomena in the aether, of whose laws we are ignorant."

Thomson chose as his means of mathematically analyzing the cathode ray an analogy with electrolysis, in which electricity was carried by charged particles called ions. Faraday in his researches on electrolysis used a quantity, e/m, which he defined as the charge of a particle, e, divided by its mass, m. Thomson devised experimental means of determining m/e. These experiments were the results of some simple mathematical deductions, no calculus was involved, which stemmed from the physical concept of particles. Since the cathode rays were negatively charged particles, the charge measured by an electrometer should equal the charge on each particle, e, times the number of particles. In addition, since the particles were assumed to have mass, when they struck a solid body the energy of the particles should be converted to heat which could be calculated as a function of the mass of the particle, m, and the velocity, v. He also calculated what the path of a particle would be in a magnetic field in terms of m/e and v. Using a group of equations, Thomson determined some crucial values by means of experiments and was then able to calculate m/e and v.

He used a second method of determining these values as a check. Using equations derived from the assumed electrostatic and magnetic characteristics of the particles, he again set up experiments to find the values for m/e and for v. It was the nature of his approach that he could not determine m and e separately but only the quantity m/e.

"From these determinations," Thomson reported, "we see that the value of m/e is independent of the nature of the gas [in the cathode tube], and that its value 10^{-7} is very small compared with the value 10^{-4}, which is the smallest value of this quantity previously known. . . ." The previously known value 10^{-4} or 0.0001 was the value determined for the hydrogen ion found from Faraday's electrolysis experiments. The smallness of the quantity m/e could be a result of either the smallness of the mass of the particle or the largeness of the charge on it. The results of previous experiments led Thomson to the belief that the cathode particles were "small compared with other molecules."

"The explanation which seems to me to account in the most simple and straightforward manner for the facts," Thomson wrote, "is founded on a view of the constitution of the chemical elements which have been favourably entertained by many chemists." He was referring to Prout's hypothesis, which had been given currency by chemists at different times during the nineteenth century. Prout had said that all matter was formed from a primordial stuff and that this stuff was the hydrogen atom. The uncertainty as to the validity of Prout's theory was due to the uncertainty of atomic weights, but once they were determined accurately, Prout's hypothesis was rejected. Now Thomson was seeking to revive this theory in a different form. He thought the molecules of the gas were split up in the intense electric field of the cathode and were formed "not into ordinary chemical atoms, but into these primordial atoms, which we shall for brevity call corpuscles. . . ." Crookes' particles were therefore not molecules as he assumed, but they were much smaller than the smallest known particle, the hydrogen atom. The particle theory now seemed to be verified for, as Thomson said, "if these corpuscles are charged with electricity and projected from the cathode by the electric field, they would behave exactly like the cathode rays."[14] The name for this new particle was later changed from corpuscle to *electron.*

Thomson had uncovered a path that was to lead physics into a wholly new and marvelous world. But could physicists be sure that Thomson had not been carried away in his speculations? How much of Thomson's results could be accepted? Previous supporters of the particle theory found further confirmation of their view. But Thomson had done much more than give further experimental proof. He had shown that this physical explanation could be quantified and that mathematically deduced results could be checked experimentally. As far as the scientific community was concerned, Thomson had done enough to settle the controversy. The electron theory would shortly represent the majority opinion. There would still be those who found the new idea incredible, if not unbelievable.

Professor G.F. Fitzgerald had heard Thomson's talk and he was among those who received it the most favorably—if cautiously. Fitzgerald wrote in May, 1897:

> I may express a hope that Prof. J. J. Thomson is quite right in his by no means impossible hypothesis. It would be the beginning of great advances in science, and the results it would be likely to lead to in the near future might easily eclipse most of the other great discoveries of the nineteenth century, and be a magnificent scientific contribution to this Jubilee year [of Queen Victoria].[15]

Encouragement and Diffusion of Science

11   Science should be encouraged; we agree because of the well-known benefits of its practical application. Examples of this benefit come easily to mind. Mention astronomy and one thinks of navigation. The physics of heat and electricity are immediately associated with manufacturing. Yet, to base the encouragement of science on its practical applications comes from the false premise that applied science is synonymous with scientific investigation. Practical applications of scientific knowledge make use of what is known and already accepted. The undefined boundary between practical applications of scientific knowledge and engineering has led to contradictory actions.

Scientific investigation is the making of theories and includes all the work involved in the forming and testing of new theories. It is the theories that give direction to research, and without them there would be no increase of scientific knowledge. What is usually meant by the encouragement of "science" is the fostering of scientific investigation, but no satisfactory method has been worked out for aiding scientific investigation. Governments have been more successful in promoting applied science.

The diffusion of science is just as serious a concern as

the encouragement of science. The two are closely related. Diffusion means the spreading of scientific ideas, first among the creative experienced scientists and then a gradual extension. The next to be influenced by new scientific ideas are the part-time investigator and the amateur. From this point science becomes popular and becomes public knowledge. Fully as important as scientific application is the absorption of scientific knowledge into the culture. This knowledge does not merely have an impact on the culture; it must become part of the culture. From Aristotle to Aquinas, to Newton, to Einstein, scientific knowledge has inevitably been a part of man's view of his world.

There never has been a policy in any country towards the encouragement and diffusion of science. There is only the influence of institutions. What the government does, what education is, and what private organizations propose to do are the influences that affect science. The changes in these institutions during the nineteenth century were what produced the change in the pursuit of scientific knowledge.

The pervading characteristic of the nineteenth century was the spread of opportunity. The enclaves of privilege in economic, social, political, and intellectual spheres were gradually opened to greater numbers of people. The ferment for this movement began with the French Revolution. The revolutionary attempts to destroy all privilege almost ruined the possibility of encouragement for any type of excellence. The foolishly short-sighted suspension of the French Academy of Science is an example. Paris remained the intellectual center of France through the nineteenth century, especially for the pursuit of science. The Academy remained the chief scientific institution in spite of attempts to diffuse scientific organizaton. The government remained highly centralized and its influence on science was concentrated in Paris. The major universities for scientific training also remained in Paris.

In Germany, the spreading of opportunity was most evident in the great increase in the number of public schools and universities. The education system, with the university at the top, was a result of the political and secular change.

In Great Britain, the growth and spread of industrialization through the country was the chief characteristic of the nineteenth century. London still remained a center, but it was not the only center for intellectual activity. The increase in this energy was most evident in Scotland, but was also discernible in the industrial centers of the provinces.

Although Russia and the United States did produce individual scientists who made important contributions, these men were exceptions in the early part of the nineteenth century since neither country had important scientific communities. The rapid growth that the United States experienced during the century had its effects in the establishment of engineering colleges and such centers of scientific research as Johns Hopkins University. Russia was the exception to the spreading of opportunity. All institutions that could have encouraged original scientific work had successfully resisted change. The oligarchical government resisted all change. The education system was outmoded. Private organizations were ineffective.

Dmitri Ivanovich Mendeleev, one of Russia's important contributors to the nineteenth century, had a career that exemplifies the limited opportunity of nineteenth century Russia. Had his mother not been so determined to have her son enter upon a scientific career and had she not the means and connections of a fairly well-to-do widow, Mendeleev would probably have spent his life as a businessman or a small town teacher. When she could not enroll her son in the university, the mother did the next best thing and entered him at the St. Petersburg Central Pedogogic Institute in the science and mathematics faculty.

Mendeleev's talent and determination opened opportunities which were available to very few in Russia at that time. After a few years as a private tutor at St. Petersburg University, he was granted permission by the Russian Minister of Public Instruction to study abroad. There was no other way of obtaining a good theoretical and experimental background. He studied with leading chemists at Paris and Heidelburg. On his return to Russia, Mendeleev was appointed professor of chemistry at the Technological Institute and later became professor of chemistry at St. Petersburg.

When service to his country and an international reputation gave Mendeleev a platform from which to advocate change in

Russian science education, he advocated a narrow technical training. In his *Remarks on Public Instruction in Russia* (1901), he wrote that "the fundamental direction of Russian education should be living and real, not based on dead languages, grammatical rules, and dialectical discussions which, without experimental control, bring self-deceit, illusion, presumption, and selfishness." Twentieth century Russia, according to Mendeleev, needed fewer Platos and more Newtons. "Classicists," he wrote, "are only fit to be landowners, capitalists, civil servants, men of letters, critics, describing and discussing, but helping only indirectly the cause of popular needs." What had his long career and international travel taught him? "We could live at the present day without a Plato, but a double number of Newtons is required to discover the secrets of nature, and to bring life into harmony without the laws of nature."[1]

France, after its revolution, made a break with its absolutist monarchy and adapted a different form of absolutist government. The new absolutist regime made thoroughgoing changes. They were determined to abolish privilege and to take positive steps toward improving living conditions for the poor. One result of the cutting of the ties between the Church and the State was a secularization of education. The revolutionaries neglected the University of Paris and established a different type of centralized university, the *Ecole Polytechnique.*

This new engineering school included a much wider area of study than the old *Ecole des Ponts et Chaussés,* which was interested primarily in what was called civil engineering. The design of bridges, roads, and canals was essential during the expansion of commerce, but by the end of the eighteenth century some Frenchmen realized that industrialization required a different type of training, for example, in mechanics and chemistry. The *Polytechnique* was devoted to the teaching of all branches of engineering. The school, against the wishes of such people as Laplace, concentrated on applied science, and scientific investigation was relegated to the *Ecole Normale.*

The *Polytechnique* became the pacesetter for education in France, and its method had its impact on the rest of Europe and the United States. The effect of this new type of education was to neglect literature and history. The product of this system was "the technical specialist who was regarded as educated because he had passed through difficult schools but who had little or no knowledge of society, its life, growth, problems and its values. . . ."[2]

How did this attempt of the Revolutionary Convention to foster applied science, or that science that could improve the physical condition of man, affect science itself? Would science flourish under this type of encouragement? Apparently it did not. At first the *Polytechnique* did make its contribution to the advance of pure science by employing the leading theoretical scientists of France as teachers. Its faculty consisted of scientific luminaries such as Lagrange, Fourier, Prony, Poinsot, Fourcroy, and Berthollet. These in turn trained the next generation of *Polytechnique* faculty, which included Poisson, Ampère, Gay-Lussac, and Arago.

These men not only aided the school by means of their reputation but students were fortunate in having men for teachers "who were the leaders of their day in research; they were productive in both pure and applied science." Science education thereby benefited by this innovation. As one historian has written: "Never before had the new recruits to science been faced with such a richness of example and attitude from which to learn."

It should have come as no surprise when Napoleon militarized the *Polytechnique*. This interference hampered the development of French engineering. French science also lost ground, and by mid-century France stood behind England and Germany. French science lost its creative surge not because the *Polytechnique* declined but because of the government's attitude towards science as exemplified by the founding of the *Polytechnique*.[3] The new government wished to encourage science, but only applied science. In spite of the fact that the leading men of science taught at the *Polytechnique*, the narrowing of the education, after a delay of one generation, could not produce good scientists. In France, after the Revolution, the state's encouragement of science produced disaster.

The decline of science in France had followed a period of rapid growth. In the first decades of the nineteenth century, "the home of the scientific spirit was France." This spirit may not have been born in France, "it was nevertheless there nursed into full growth and vigour."[4] French science was characterized as being closely linked with mathematics. Since the formation of the *Académie des Sciences* in the seventeenth century, French science had been centralized in Paris and reliant upon government support. With the change of government after the Revolution, the support changed in nature and French science became less imaginative. But it was the French "scientific spirit" that was diffused throughout Europe in the nineteenth century. This spirit underwent a change due to the adaption to the peculiar institutions and to the intellectual outlook of the importing country. Science, for example, in Germany was diffused through the university system, which was much different from the French system. In Germany, the French exact spirit of science met with idealistic philosophy known as *Naturphilosophie.* Science was not to be the same again after its collision with German philosophy.

When it was said that every German man of science was a philosopher, what was meant was that he had been indoctrinated in his student days into some school of philosophy and for the rest of their lives most fought this indoctrination. Many of Germany's first rank scientists belonged to or were influenced by the school known as *Naturphilosophie.*[5]

Like all philosophies, *Naturphilosophie* is difficult to summarize in a few words. It is a philosophy that contrasts with the English view of the world, as consisting of matter in motion, and the French scientists use of mathematics as the only means of describing the world. To the *Naturphilosophen*, the world consisted of an essential unity that flowed from God. *Geist,* the transcendent Absolute, achieved realization in the material world, and it was their purpose to trace this process. "Nature is to be visible intelligence," wrote Schelling, one of the founders of *Naturphilosophie,* "and intelligence invisible nature."

Nature, therefore, is not a collection of "dead" particles in motion. It is alive and the result of dialectical unity of active forces. The true scientist, therefore, must deal with these inner forces rather than the husk of its phenomenal appearance. Nature is process. "Summed up shortly, the characteristics of *Naturphilosophie* may be set down as a dynamic view of Nature and an application of the principle of development in the widest sense."[6]

These ideas were denounced in France and unknown in England, but in Germany the advocates of *Naturphilosophie* spread their influence over the universities because they occupied the important chairs of philosophy and they could be found in most of the learned societies.

German scientists such as Justus Liebig usually completed their training abroad. Liebig, like many of the others, rejected the speculative methods of *Naturphilosophie* and fell under the spell of the empirical and experimental method. The metamorphosis was described by Liebig:

> What influenced me most in the French lectures was their inner truthfulness and the careful omission of all mere semblance of explanations: it was a complete contrast to the German lectures, in which, through a preponderence of the deductive process, the scientific doctrine had quite lost its rigid coherence. . . .[7]

In his agricultural chemistry, Liebig referred to the interchange between the soil and all living organisms. This concept, which was central to his approach to organic chemistry, exhibits the influence of *Naturphilosophie,* which referred to organic transformations and the interrelationship of all organs in a larger organism.

There is much to be said for the provocation of universal concepts like *Naturphilosophie.* "For if laboratory analysis and experiment protected the German scientists against excessively speculative methods and metaphysical speculation generally," one historian believed, "*Naturphilosophie,* learned in their youth provided them with an endless variety of stimulating ideas."[8]

The German university system became a model in the nineteenth century for those who sought to produce a blend between the encouragement of the advancement of science and the diffusion of science. Merz referred to the university as "this great engine of thought" and believed that "this vast organization for intellectual work" deserved a foremost place in the history of thought. The university that the Germans developed was the primary factor in that country's scientific hegemony. Where dozens of scientists flocked to the laboratories of Berzelius in Sweden and Gay-Lussac in Paris, thousands of scientists from all over the world converged on the German universities in Berlin, Giessen, and Göttingen.

The great diversity and number of German universities were equal to the number and variety of German principalities. Control by the state gradually supplanted the ecclesiastical domination, which dated from the Middle Ages. Each of the states developed on its own a complete system of education. In Wurtemberg, for example, which had a population of about two-thirds of London's, there were as many elementary schools as there were parishes, 450 industrial schools for girls, 523 farming schools, 108 trade schools, 76 industrial academies in which pure, mixed, and applied science were taught, a great agricultural college at Hohenheim, a building-trades' college at Stuttgart, and at the pinnacle of the whole system there was a Polytechnic University at Stuttgart.[9]

The number of industrial training schools without doubt reflects the princes' concern for the industrialization of their state. But the university was the jewel in the prince's crown rather than an instrument of government. In 1808 Prussia appointed Wilhelm von Humboldt, scholar and statesman, as the head of its school-system. In France, after the Revolution, the university was harnessed to the state and was seen as an essential element in producing economic and social reform. Humboldt's selection "in itself gave evidence of the fact that Prussia had no inclination to imitate the conqueror in these matters." Humboldt organized a new University of Berlin where, according to a German historian, "professors were not to be teaching and examining state officials, but independent scholars."[10]

Diversification became the keynote of the German universities, and this spreading out affected scientific work. In contrast, centralization was the chief characteristic of French research, and insularity was the determining feature of English thought. The large number of universities in Germany was a direct outcome of the Protestant Reformation there in the sixteenth century. Each sect required at least one university for the training of its clergy. With the secularization of the university came a different type of specialization. For example, in the nineteenth century Königsberg became a center for the study of mathematical physics, and when Johannes Müller received an appointment to the university at Berlin in 1833, it became a center for physiology. In a like manner, Giessen became the center for chemistry because of Liebig's work there.

Until the eighteenth century the German university was comprised of three faculties: theology, law, and medicine. The first two prepared young men for the church or the state, and the third faculty was training for an independent profession. A fourth faculty, the philosophical faculty, was added for training in the new profession of science. The University of Göttingen, founded in 1734, was the first to have a philosophical faculty.

The philosophical faculty as conceived in Germany during the nineteenth century was similar to the Greek view of philosophy as being an all inclusive study that took in not only cosmology and physics but logic and metaphysics, in addition to ethics and politics. The German modification of the Greek idea was that philosophy entailed original research.

For the most part, the philosophical faculty was given the responsibility of preparing students for the professional training they received in the other three faculties. The philosophical faculty inherited the responsibility of training teachers for the German schools of higher education when teaching in the higher schools ceased to be an adjunct of the clerical profession. In the nineteenth century the philosophical faculty had three responsibilities. It was "(1) an institution for scientific research in the entire realm of nature and history; (2) a general scientific preparatory school for the students of the other faculties; (3) a scientific professional school for advanced teachers."[11]

Merz characterized the German universities as the most "powerful organization for the diffusion of knowledge." Not only were they increasing in number and in enrollment but they were linked in with the high schools and technical schools. An example of this close allegiance was the fact that Heinrich Hertz, a prize student of Helmholtz, was willing to teach in a technical high school. A further indication of the opportunities for a scientist at a high school is the fact that while teaching at one Hertz did his research on electromagnetic waves. "Every school has its watchword," Merz wrote, "in which its leading thought, its ideal, is embodied." For the German intellectual of the nineteenth century "the watchword" was *Wissenschaft,* which may be translated as "science." But it meant much more to a German. For instance, there was the science of philosophical criticism, of historical criticism, of Biblical criticism, and of philology. "All these professed to have methods as definite, aims as lofty, and a style as pure, as the exact sciences brought with them." According to Merz, the concept of *Wissenschaft* was the essential part of the German contribution to science.[12]

The German student was supposed to learn to do independent scientific work. For this purpose, the seminar was introduced, and also the teaching laboratory, such as Liebig had begun at Giessen. "The philosophical faculty . . . is purely theoretical. Its teachers are the true exponents of scientific research and its students are the scholars of the future," a member of one of those faculties wrote in 1902.

What was imbued in the student by this process was the conviction that "the first and essential requisite for this profession [teaching] is thorough scholarship." And not only was this true of the university teacher but "the German gymnasial teacher looks upon himself wholly as a scholar, at least at the beginning of his career when university memories are most keenly alive in him."[13]

The whole German educational system, which included the universities and the high schools, not only was the means of diffusing the latest in scientific knowledge but it was "an equally powerful organisation for research, and for increasing knowledge." The system was the best means of encouraging the increase of scientific knowledge. The universities and high schools contained "a well-trained army of workers, standing under the intellectual generalship of a few great leading minds." The German belief in the joining of teaching with research was the essence of its strength and the primary contribution to the advancement of science. "The university system, in one word, not only teaches knowledge, but above all it teaches *research,*" Merz wrote. "This is its pride and the foundation of its fame."[14]

But was the encouragement of science, the advancement of learning, the primary responsibility of the university? Thomas

Young, who proposed the wave theory of light, was educated in Germany in Göttingen and in England at Cambridge. In answer to a criticism of English universities in 1810, Young wrote that "it must be remembered that the *advancement* of learning is by no means the principal object of an academical institution: the *diffusion* of a respectable share of instruction in literature and in the sciences among those classes which hold the highest situations and have the most extensive influence in the State is an object of more importance to the public than the discovery of new truths. . . ."[15]

Tradition, reinforced by convictions such as Young's, slowed change at the English universities. But in the United States, with little of its own tradition and with an opportunity to start fresh, some institutions experimented with the German model. At the opening of Johns Hopkins University in 1876, Thomas Henry Huxley applauded that university's plans for instruction. "I rejoice to observe that the encouragement of research occupies so prominent a place in your official documents," he said, and summed up his views this way:

> I know of no more difficult practical problem than the discovery of a method of encouraging and supporting the original investigator without opening the door to nepotism and jobbery. My own conviction is admirably summed up in the passage of your president's address, "that the best investigators are usually those who have also the responsibilities of instruction, gaining thus the incitement of colleagues, the encouragement of pupils, and the observation of the public."[16]

The German man of science was usually part of the university system. That system not only supported him but, more important than that, the system made the teaching of science a main source for the encouragement of individual investigation on the part of the professor and his students.

No such encouragement could have been expected from the English universities, especially from Oxford and Cambridge. At mid-century, public opinion was cutting at the impenetrable crust of tradition, which had isolated the two universities from society and from change. The journals charged that the two were "citadels of political prejudice and sectarian exclusiveness." It was pointed out that there were no professors of Latin, or of English literature, or of logic and metaphysics, or of modern languages at Cambridge. Neither of the universities prepared men for the practice of law. In 1850 a Royal Commission of Inquiry was appointed to investigate the two universities and the reports of the commission, which were published in 1852, corroborated the criticism that had been directed at the institutions.[17]

All education was at a low ebb and, in spite of what some believed, science had not been singled out for neglect. Attention was directed at the low state of science teaching in the English universities earlier in the century but that was due to the envy of the German success. Oxford professors of experimental philosophy, comparative anatomy, chemistry, mineralogy, geology, botany, and astronomy made an effort in 1839 to introduce reform in the examination system. Attendance in these classes had dwindled during the period from 1819 to 1838. One successful English scientist, Charles Lyell, wrote: "After the year 1839, we may consider three-fourths of the Sciences, still nominally taught at Oxford, to have been virtually exiled from the University. . . ."[18]

The criticism did promote some change at England's two universities. A laboratory course in chemistry was begun at Cambridge in 1852, but adequate facilities were not available until after 1863. A chair in experimental physics was established at Oxford in 1866. The mathematical tripos at Cambridge were changed in 1868 to include questions on heat, light, electricity, and magnetism. That change in the examinations was part of the stimulus that led to the establishment of the Cavendish Laboratory at Cambridge in 1871. The Cavendish Laboratory was to become important, almost immediately, in the diffusion of science through the experimental experience offered to physics and non-physics students. The laboratory also became the center for some important original work by such men as Rayleigh and J. J. Thomson, but that was not until late in the century.

In 1895 Cambridge established a new category of student known as "Research Student." They were awarded an M.A. after two years residence and after submitting a thesis based on original research. That this move was to place Cambridge in a world-wide competition for original minds can be seen by the group of men who hurried to matriculate in 1895. Among them was Ernest Rutherford from New Zealand, who became the fourth Cavendish Professor. After a few years, Cambridge changed the degree to Ph.D. because it was found that the Cambridge graduates, since they were not entitled to be called "doctor," were at a disadvantage when competing with graduates from German universities.[19]

Cambridge's action was an important change for the training of physicists. The university had hitherto been giving a theoretical training in mathematics to science students. Those who were interested in experimental physics had to obtain their experience elsewhere.

Notwithstanding the criticism, British scientists were making contributions to scientific theory that were greater in originality and in possibility for future development than those made by scientists from any other country. The first half-century witnessed the introduction of new theories by John Dalton, Thomas Young, Humphry Davy, Michael Faraday, and James Prescott Joule. Of these, only Young had had university training in science. The British had nothing to compare with the French or Germans for the training of scientists, and this condition resulted in what Merz called the "casual and accidental" aspect of the great ideas contributed by British men of science.

The source of British originality, which was the primary characteristic of British science, at least during the first half-century, was their intellectual insularity and determined individualism. British scientists did not believe that they had to be attached to a large institution, whether it be a university or research laboratory, in order to achieve success as investigators. Tertius Lydgate, of George Eliot's *Middlemarch*, was the image, apparently, that most Englishmen had of scientific pursuit in the early part of the century.

Maxwell described Faraday's originality as a result of his want of opportunity. Faraday had a limited knowledge of mathematics and a poor grounding in astronomy. He regarded Newton as a "sacred mystery" and treatises that were important in his study of electricity and magnetism, like Poisson and Ampère, were closed to Faraday because he did not command enough mathematical facility. Maxwell wrote:

> Thus Faraday, with his penetrating intellect, his devotion to science, and his opportunities for experiment was debarred from following the course of thought which had led to the achievements of the French philosophers, and was obliged to explain the phenomena to himself by means of a symbolism which he could understand, instead of adopting what had hitherto been the only tongue of the learned.[20]

When Faraday abandoned "the only tongue of the learned" he invented a method of representing magnetism by means of his lines of force, which was fruitful to the study of electromagnetism.

What prevented the intellectual isolation and the strong individualism of the English scientist from turning into mere eccentricity? Merz believed that it was the close association with nature, which "rewarded and refreshed him by a novel inspiration—she had lifted her veil to his loving eye and revealed to him one of her secrets. The individualism of English science has been tempered by its naturalism."[21]

Helmholtz, who admitted that he had learned much from his experience in England, believed that the drive of English scientists came from the fact that they came from "different classes of society and of the most different occupations." This variety of background produced a tendency towards individualism and "practical fruitfulness," whereas on the Continent most of the scientists belonged "to a peculiar class, more isolated from the other classes of men, more connected by its interests and occupations." Therefore, French and Germans developed "scientific schools, with all the advantages and disadvantages which tradition and the discipline of such a school tend to produce."[22]

During this period England was undergoing economic change as a result of the rapid expansion of its economy: new wealth, new opportunities in all fields, and a new mobility in which an unusually capable intellect might aspire to better things. One need only follow the paths that Davy, Dalton, or Faraday took to see that the broadening of opportunity produced by social and economic change was essential to their success.

A man with uncommon views depends on having channels open to him that will enable him to find an outlet for his ideas. Will his work lie unknown and unused like Cavendish's? Or will some journal, preferably one with a wide circulation, give him a platform? Perhaps some professional organization will permit him to give a paper.

Men who promote original ideas need not be political, religious, or social radicals, but they are most often outside of the Establishment. William Thomson came from a middle class background. His father was a professor at the University of Glasgow. The father was a political liberal and actively worked to repeal the requirement for a religious oath at the university. The son, William, was provided with a first-class education at Cambridge and abroad. The father managed to pay for such luxuries for his talented son by means of the exercise of strict economy. (See the many father-to-son letters exhorting the son to be thrifty in Silvanus P. Thompson's biography of Lord Kelvin.)

The family means was not large enough to supply William Thomson with an independence to pursue scientific investigations. William Thomson had shown scientific brilliance and exceptional mathematical ability early in his life, but his father worried about his son's "experimental requirements." Experimental ability was valued at the University of Glasgow as indicating a European-type preparation in science. This ability was referred to as the "popular part of Natural Philosophy" since experiments were invaluable in illustrating lectures. William Thomson's father warned him that his Cambridge education might have neglected to develop his "power of easy expression or of commanding the attention of an audience," attributes that were considered essential to one who would hold the Chair of Natural Philosophy at Glasgow. William was attentive to his father's advice and was appointed in 1846.

Many other men found a scientific haven at the Scottish

universities. Whereas in England it was common for scientists to work outside of the university in Scotland, first-rate scientists like Gregory, Simson, Maclaurin, Playfair, Black, Thomson, Leslie, Brewster, and Forbes were all university professors. The changes taking place in Scotland at that time made it a stimulating place to be. Merz has referred to the relationship between England and Scotland as an "intellectual intercourse and exchange which has existed all through this century [the nineteenth] between the invigorating spirit of the north and the more conservative spirit of the southern portion of the island."[23]

In England the universities did not play any role in the encouragement and diffusion of science until the last part of the century. Scientists interested in research had to be resourceful in finding ways of supporting themselves. The lack of any kind of regular agency to provide either public or private support for English scientists limited their number, but those who were ingenious enough to support themselves were those who supplied the originality of English science.

The British government may have been cool to science during the first half of the century, and the citadels of the aristocracy may have ignored science altogether, but science was popular with the masses. The industrial workmen throughout Great Britain had a curiosity about science which they attempted to satisfy by attending public lectures. By mid-century it is estimated that there were 600 mechanics institutes with approximately 100,000 members. These members were interested in furthering their education and they especially wanted to know more about science. A good livelihood along with popular recognition was possible to those scientists like Humphry Davy, Michael Faraday, and John Tyndall, who were good speakers and demonstrators of science.

One person in the government who was interested in promoting science was Prince Albert, who did much to make the Great Exhibition of 1851 possible. At the close of the exhibition it was the Prince's wish to use the surplus funds to found an institution for furthering international progress in science and technology. The Prince's importance in the government was not great enough to carry such a project through in the face of the indifference of the government and the learned societies. His proposals were not carried out until much after his death when the Imperial College of Science and Technology was founded and the Science Museums were established.[24]

Should the English government have encouraged science? Yes, Charles Babbage believed, and "to those who measure the question of national encouragement of science by its value in pounds, shillings, and pence" Babbage cited an example of a loss to the country "of between two and three millions sterling." The loss was due to an error in calculating annuity tables. "Half the interest of half that loss," Babbage estimated, "judiciously applied to the encouragement of mathematical science, would, in a few years, have rendered utterly impossible such expensive errors." To Babbage, it seemed a terrible waste of mental power to allow John Dalton "to be employed in the drudgery of elementary instruction." Why that was as improvident a waste, Babbage claimed, as it would have been to allow the Duke of Wellington "to employ his life in drilling recruits, instead of planning campaigns."

The British government should support science, according to Babbage, but could it? No. The triumphs of an Archimedes, Newton, or a Dalton were so infrequent that it would be unlikely for a government to do any good in encouraging the advance of science. "Too extraordinary to be frequent," were the appearances of scientific theorists that, Babbage believed, "they must be left, if they are to be encouraged at all, to some direct interference of the government."[25]

That there was a decline in the state of science in England was a common belief. A book published by Babbage in 1830 gave voice to a general concern. The book was titled *Reflections on the Decline of Science in England and on Some of its Causes.* Others agreed with Babbage that the government had been neglectful in its encouragement of science, especially as compared with continental nations. A Scotsman, Sir David Brewster, wrote in the *Quarterly Review* of 1830, that the British Isles did not contain a single scientist "who bears the lowest title that is given to the lowest benefactor of the nation," or "enjoys a pension, or allowance, or a sinecure capable of supporting him and his family in the humblest circumstances," nor finally was there a British scientist who "enjoys the favour of his sovereign or the friendship of his ministers."[26]

There was rebuttal made to these charges. One pamphlet was titled *On the alleged Decline of Science in England* and its title page said only that it was by a "Foreigner." Faraday wrote an introduction for this defense of the way science was being treated in England. In the introduction, Faraday wrote that "all must allow that it is an extraordinary circumstance for English character to be attacked by natives and defended by foreigners."[27] Faraday apparently did not feel neglected by the government. This publication appeared in 1831, when Faraday could have used a grant in aid of his research.

The criticisms leveled by Babbage and others are interesting not only because this discontent was the force behind the formation of the British Association for the Advancement of Science but also because these men were presumably expressing the feelings of other English scientists. What did Babbage and those like him want? He had said that direct aid from the government was impractical. Brewster made mention of "favour of his sovereign" and other types of reward and recognition. This type of encouragement is after the fact, that is, after the scientist has made his contribution is the only time one can expect his sovereign to reward him with favors. After-the-fact recognition actually does very little to promote the advancement of science since it is too remote to be of any real help to struggling young scientists.

Babbage was witnessing a rise in the status of new professionals and new classes. He was also a radical himself who favored a rise in status of the lower classes. The entrenchment of privilege and the obstruction of progress was epitomized, in Babbage's view, by the Royal Society. "The Society has, for years, been managed by a *party*, or *coterie*. . .", Babbage charged. "The great object of this, as of all other parties, has been to maintain itself in power, and to divide, as far as it could, all the good things amongst its members." This group consisted of men of "very moderate talent" and as a party, Babbage wrote, they "have always praised each other most highly—have invariably opposed all improvements in the Society, all change in the mode of management; and have maintained, that all those who wished for any alteration were factious. . . ."

There were several reasons why scientists formed learned societies, Babbage believed. Among them was the desire to supply a means of publishing the results of their investigations. The Royal Society by 1830, Babbage pointed out, had become most ineffective and inefficient in carrying out this mission. Another way that a learned society served in encouraging science was that membership in the select society was the goal of ambitious young scientists. But Babbage pointed out that "if at any time, a multitude of persons having no sort of knowledge of science are admitted, it must cease to be sought after as an object of ambition by men of science, and the class of persons to whom it will become an object of desire will be less intellectual."

For membership in a learned society to bestow any distinction, the list of members must be kept short. Yet Babbage found that while in France one out of every 427,000 people was a member of the Institute, in England one out of every 32,000 inhabitants was a member of the Royal Society. Or as he said, "A member of the Institute of France will be more than thirteen times more rare in his country than a Fellow of the Royal Society is in England." On top of that the roles of the Royal Society were heavy with the number of titled personages and of that number only one, Sir Humphry Davy, had earned his title by means of his scientific activity.

The Royal Society had become the exclusive domain of the aristocracy in many ways according to Babbage. Membership was a matter of being put up by the people who were members of the "party" and the subscription required of members was so large as to "prevent many men of real science from entering the Society, and is a very severe tax on those who do so; for very few indeed of the cultivators of science rank amongst the wealthy classes. . . . I should conjecture," Babbage wrote bitterly, ". . . that it is not unusual for gentlemen in the country to order their agents in London to take measures for putting them up at the Royal Society."

His attack on the hold that the privileged classes had on science was an appeal to public opinion.

> . . . with the conviction that discussion is the firmest ally of truth,—and with the confidence that nothing but the full expression of public opinion can remove the evils that chill the enthusiasm, and cramp the energies of the science of England.[28]

Britain differed from France and Germany of the nineteenth century because in Britain, as Merz noted, "there exists no central authority which can create powerful organizations or disburse public means without the distinctly and repeatedly expressed support of a large section of the people."[29]

In spite of the forceful public attack on the Royal Society, Babbage could not have had much hope of reforming that venerable organization, especially since the entrenched party, which he attacked as being the cause of the decline of science, was not answerable to public opinion. Neither did Babbage have in mind the formation of a public society for the diffusion of science. Had he had something like that in mind there were already organizations like the Royal Institution and the Society for the Diffusion of Useful Knowledge. These societies had as their mission the spread of new scientific knowledge to the masses. What Babbage did have in mind was a society that would be competitive to the Royal Society, but one whose membership would not be thrown open to all who could pay the fee but only to those men who "cultivated the sciences."

Only cultivators of science were permitted to join the newly formed Society of German Naturalists and Natural Philosophers. Babbage noted: "All those who had printed a certain number of sheets of their inquiries on these subjects [botany and medicine] were considered members of this academy."[30] The first meeting of the German organization was held in 1822 with forty members attending. Babbage reported in the *Edinburgh Journal of Science* that the 1828 meeting of the German Naturalists had an attendance of 377.

Because of the strong individualistic streak of the British

scientists, the best method of encouraging science was for them to band together and encourage each other as the Germans had done. The British Association for the Advancement of Science was to be markedly more successful than the Society of German Naturalists, because in the early nineteenth century the BAAS was all that British scientists had. The center of German science remained in the universities and the Society meetings were more like social gatherings.

The first printed *Report of the British Association for the Advancement of Science* published reviews of recent advances and actual state of several of the sciences.

The "Recommendations" for lines to be pursued applied to two different levels in the cultivation of science. For example, the chemical committee, in the 1831 *Report,* recommended that the relative weights of several elements be accurately determined so as to "insure the reasonable assent of all competent and unprejudiced judges." The Association believed that "experienced chemists" were required for this work, whereas the need for some additional meteorological and botanical researches which belonged "to a lower order of facts, are open to a much wider class of observers, and are capable of being extended through all parts of the country by the exertions of individuals, and still more effectively by those of Societies."[31]

It was just this type of distinction between the two levels of conducting science that Charles Babbage wanted made. He charged that the Royal Society had not differentiated between mere observations and original discoveries. All too often, Babbage noted, the Royal Society had given its honorary medals to the observers who, after all, were the lowly drudges of science. To demonstrate this point Babbage quoted a letter from the Astronomer Royal who was requesting assistants:

> But to carry on such investigations, I want indefatigable, hardworking, and above all, obedient drudges (for so I must call them, although they are drudges of a superior order), men who will be contented to pass half their day in using their hands and eyes in the mechanical act of observing, and the remainder of it in the dull process of calculation.[32]

The Yorkshire Philosophical Society thought that the British Association would link societies as well as individual scientists "in a common participation and divison of labour." Efforts thereby could be directed towards the answering of some questions, "the data of which are *geographically* distributed, and require to be collected by local observations extended over a whole country." The provincial societies would benefit in pursuing a common objective. Progress reports made from year to year at a national meeting "in the presence of an assembly concentrating a great part of the scientific talent of the nation" would cause the "kindling of an increased ardour of emulous activity." To the Yorkshire Philosophical Society it seemed "impossible that the deputies of any Society should attend such meetings without bringing back into its bosom an enlargement of views, and communicating to its members new lights of knowledge, new motives for inquiry, and new encouragement to perseverance."[33]

One more factor lent importance to the British Association by virtue of its broadly based membership. Charles Lyell wrote Charles Darwin in 1838 that he was aware of the shortcomings of the British Association, where philosophers turned "public orators." "But I am convinced," Lyell wrote, "although it is not the way I love to spend my own time, that in this country no importance is attached to any body of men who do not make occasional demonstrations of their strength in public meetings. It is a country where . . . nothing is to be got in the way of homage or influence, or even a fair share of power, without agitation."[34]

Babbage's criticism of the Royal Society was that its membership had grown so large that it was no longer a distinction to be a Fellow. He also found fault with the Royal Society's practice of granting awards to persons who had done no more for science than make some observations. Babbage contended that the recognition should go to scientists who had done original work and by that he meant the formation of new theories.

The membership in the British Association was larger than in the Royal Society, which had grown in membership but was basing admission on social, rather than scientific, criteria. The British Association did not attempt to restrict itself to an elite of scientists who were making original contributions to theory, as Babbage had wanted the Royal Society to do. Instead the British Association was a vast democratic institution made up of anyone who took their science seriously enough to devote time and energy to its pursuit. The Association specifically denied any attempt to compete with the Royal Society or any other organization. In the opening statement of the "Objects of the Association" appeared this disclaimer: "The Association contemplates no interference with the ground occupied by other Institutions."

The British Association has to be assessed on the basis of the announced intentions. There were three objects: the first was "to give a stronger impulse and a more systematic direction to scientific inquiry." The open request that scientists pursue certain lines of investigation and the organization of nationwide search for more data on such fields as meteorology and geology was in keeping with this first objective. This appeared to be the best way of getting the drudge-like work of science done in Britain. On the Continent this work was being done by graduate students and technologists connected with institutes. The danger that the Association faced was that it would be swamped by a welter of information. Certainly, all of the instrument readings which poured in were not important or worth keeping, but who was to judge? The army of cultivators was working independently without the type of supervision that one expects in a laboratory. The BAAS would have to keep information that was not only affirmation of established theories but it had to see to it that new data that may have opened the path to entirely new theories was preserved. The exercise of this kind of judgment is never completely successful. The British Association has been successful in many fields in giving a "more systematic direction to scientific inquiry" wherever it has avoided being swamped by data.

The second object was "to promote the intercourse of those who cultivate Science in different parts of the British Empire. . . ." The leading lights of the scientific world attended BAAS meetings. Acquaintances were renewed and information exchanged by these men. Since these meetings were the only place that British workers in science could exchange ideas, the Association did fulfill a need here.

The third object of the Association was "to obtain a more general attention to the objects of science, and a removal of any disadvantages of a public kind, which impede its progress." This statement does not mean government support of science but rather that government stand out of the way of scientific progress. The first meeting of the BAAS was told that "perhaps the most effectual method of promoting science is by removing the obstacles which oppose its progress." The speech was by the first president of the Association, who went on to say:

> We all know, that the laws of this country,—I mean in particular the fiscal laws of this country,—offered numerous obstacles to scientific improvements. I will name only one instance. In the science of optics very serious obstacles are found to result from the regulations relative to the manufacture of glass. I mention only this; but it must occur to many of the persons present, that there are various other instances, in which the laws interfere materially with the progress of science.[35]

As a political pressure group, the BAAS was bound to have some effect, particularly because of the large membership scattered over the country. Of additional political consequence was the fact that the BAAS chose to associate itself with the growing manufacturing centers in Britain. Babbage suggested in 1832 that meetings of the Association be held in places likely to bring "theoretical science into contact with that practical knowledge on which the wealth of the country depends."[36] If the Royal Society was associated with the mercantile interests of the country through its control of the post of Astronomer Royal and of the appointments to the Board of Longitude, the BAAS was to be associated with manufacturing. The list of cities where subsequent meetings were held coincides with the list of the leading industrial centers of Great Britain.

The United States in many ways repeated the pattern of growth of scientific organizations begun in Britain. The American Association for the Advancement of Science was founded in 1848 and like its counterpart, the BAAS, had a broadly based membership, which included amateurs, and therefore was mainly useful in the diffusion of science. The National Academy of Sciences in the United States was purposely established to bring together the scientific elite of the United States. Membership was at first limited to fifty leading men of science. The experiment in the United States was unsuccessful in advancing original scientific research. Organizations can aid in diffusing science but not encouraging it.

The growth of scientific knowledge depends on a constant source of new information and new ideas. The vitality of nineteenth century science was to a considerable degree due to the variety of these sources. France provided the base or traditional approach. The work of Fourier and Ampère was an example.

The spreading opportunities brought Germany into the arena. Its peculiar contribution was *Naturphilosophie* and *Wissenschaft*. These ideas were modified and spread by means of the university system. The university, as Germany had shown, could provide a broad base of scientific intellectuals.

England had its individualism to boast of in the early part of the century as the source of highly original ideas. Contrast the novelty of Joule's ideas with the traditionalism of Fourier. But as the century wore on, the individualists found that they had to go to the university for training in the higher mathematics. The result of British education was a blending of physical imagination and mathematical acumen in such men as Maxwell and William Thomson.

The variety of the sources of ideas by different national institutions produced differences of opinion. It was through the effect of controversies carried on across national boundaries that new theories were forged. The international exchange at the same time encouraged scientific investigation and promoted the diffusion of scientific knowledge.

Notes

CHAPTER ONE

1. Bern Dibner, *Alessandro Volta and the Electric Battery* (New York: Franklin Watts, 1964), p.131.
2. Sir Edmund Whittaker, *A History of the Theories of Aether and Electricity* (New York: Philosophical Library, 1951), Vol. I, pp. 68-69.
3. *Ibid.*, p. 70.
4. Dibner, *op. cit.*, p. 111.
5. *Ibid.*, p. 124.
6. *Ibid.*, p. 123.
7. William F. Magie, *A Source Book in Physics* (1st ed.; New York: McGraw-Hill, 1935), see article on William Nicholson.
8. John Theodore Merz, *A History of European Thought in the Nineteenth Century* (London: William Blackwood and Sons, 1896), Vol. I, p. 249n.
9. Whittaker, *op. cit.*, Vol. I. pp. 74-75.
10. Description of the establishment of magnetic stations throughout the world is in William Whewell, *History of the Inductive Sciences, From the Earliest to the Present Times* (Rev. ed.; London: John W. Parker, 1847), Vol. III, pp. 67-70.

11. *Ibid.*, p. 76.
12. Magie, *op. cit.*, see article on Oersted.
13. *Ibid.*, see article on Ampère.

CHAPTER TWO

1. *The Scientific Papers of James Prescott Joule* (Physical Society of London, 1884), Vol. I, p. 300.
2. James Bryant Conant, ed., *Harvard Case Studies in Experimental Science* (Cambridge: Harvard University Press, 1957), Vol. I, p. 189.
3. Joseph Fourier, *The Analytical Theory of Heat,* trans. by Alexander Freeman (Cambridge: University Press, 1878), p. 26.
4. *Ibid.*, p. 1.
5. *Ibid.*, p. 14.
6. *Ibid.*, pp. 1-2.
7. *Ibid.*, pp. 16-17.
8. James Clerk Maxwell, *Theory of Heat* (London: Longmans, Green, 1872), p. 238.
9. Fourier, *op. cit.*, pp. 20-21.
10. *Ibid.*, pp. 7-8.
11. *Ibid.*, p. 13.
12. H. Poincaré, *Science and Hypothesis* (New York: Charles Scribner's Sons, 1907), pp. 158-159.
13. *Report of the Fifth Meeting of the British Association for the Advancement of Science,* held at Dublin in 1835 (London: John Murray, 1836), pp. 29-30.
14. *Scientific Papers of Joule,* Vol. I, p. 14.
15. *Ibid.*, p. 27.
16. *Ibid.*, p. 60.
17. *Ibid.*, pp. 157-158.
18. Silvanus P. Thompson, *The Life of William Thomson, Baron Kelvin of Largs* (London: Macmillan, 1910), Vol. I, p. 264.
19. Sir William Thomson, *Mathematical and Physical Papers* (Cambridge: University Press, 1882), Vol. I, pp. 102-103.
20. Sir William Thomson, *Reprint of Papers on Electrostatics and Magnetism* (2nd ed.; London: Macmillan, 1884), p. 423n.
21. J. G. Crowther, *British Scientists of the Nineteenth Century* (London: Kegan Paul, Trench, Trubner, 1935), p. 192.
22. Magie, *op. cit.*, pp. 198, 202.
23. Thomson, *Mathematical and Physical Papers,* Vol. I, p. 176.
24. *Ibid.*, p. 181.

CHAPTER THREE

1. Michael Faraday, *Experimental Researches in Electricity* (London: Richard and John Edward Taylor, 1839), Vol. I, p. 2.
2. Sir William Robert Grove *et al.*, *The Correlation and Conservation of Forces: A Series of Expositions* (New York: D. Appleton, 1869), p. 377.
3. W. D. Nivens, ed., *The Scientific Papers of James Clerk Maxwell* (Paris: Librairie Scientifique, 1927), Vol. II, p. 318.
4. Faraday, *op. cit.*, Vol. I, p. 16.
5. Sir John A. Fleming, *The Alternate Current Transformer, In Theory and Practice* (New York: D. Van Nostrand, 1900), Vol. I, p. 4.
6. Faraday, *op. cit.*, Vol. I, pp. 32-33.
7. *Ibid.*, pp. 363-364.
8. Merz, *op. cit.*, Vol. I, p. 266n.

CHAPTER FOUR

1. Thompson, *op. cit.*, Vol. I, p. 241.
2. Nivens, *op. cit.*, Vol. II, p. 456.
3. Leicester and Klickstein, *A Source Book in Chemistry 1400-1900* (New York: McGraw-Hill, 1952), pp. 199, 197.
4. C. Berthollet, "Researches respecting the Laws of Affinity," *Philosophical Magazine*, Vol. 9 (1801), pp. 146-147.
5. Leicester and Klickstein, *op. cit.*, p. 204.
6. William Charles Henry, *Memoirs of the Life and Scientific Researches of John Dalton* (London: Printed for the Cavendish Society, 1854), pp. 59-60.
7. *Ibid.*, p. 15.
8. *Ibid.*, pp. 61, 142-143, 144, 29-30.
9. *Ibid.*, p. 169.
10. John Dalton *et al.*, *Foundations of the Atomic Theory, Alembic Club Reprints No.2* (London: Gurney and Jackson, 1923), p. 5.
11. Peter Ewart, "Observations on Mr. Dalton's Theory of Chemical Composition," *Annals of Philosophy*, Vol. VI (July-Dec., 1815), p. 374n.
12. *Alembic Club Reprints No. 2*, pp. 25-26.
13. *Ibid.*, p. 42.
14. *Ibid.*, pp. 35, 39.
15. Leicester and Klickstein, *op. cit.*, pp. 216-217.
16. Henry, *op. cit.*, pp. 90-91.

17. John Davy, ed., *The Collected Works of Sir Humphry Davy, Bart.* (London: Smith Elder, 1839), Vol. V, pp. 328n, 330n.
18. *Ibid.*, Vol. I, pp. 59-60.
19. *Ibid.*, p. 117.
20. Humphry Davy, "The Bakerian Lecture, on some chemical Agencies of Electricity," *Philosophical Transactions of the Royal Society of London*, Vol. 97 (1807), p. 54.
21. Davy, *Collected Works*, Vol. V, p. 433.
22. Henry, *op. cit.*, p. 171.
23. Davy, *Collected Works*, Vol. V, pp. 434-435.
24. Ernst von Meyer, *A History of Chemistry, From Earliest Times to the Present Day, Being Also an Introduction to the Study of Science* (3rd ed.; London: Macmillan, 1906), pp. 250-251.
25. *Ibid.*, p. 206n.
26. *Ibid.*, p. 221n.
27. J. J. Berzelius, "Essay on the Cause of Chemical Proportions, and on some circumstances relating to them; together with a short and easy method of expressing them," *Annals of Philosophy*, Vol. II (1813), pp. 444-445.
28. J. J. Berzelius, "An Address to those Chemists who wish to examine the Laws of Chemical Proportions, and the Theory of Chemistry in general," *Annals of Philosophy*, Vol. V (Jan.-June, 1815), p. 122.
29. Charles A. Wurtz, *The History of Chemical Theory, from the age of Lavoisier to the present time*, trans. and ed. by H. Watts (London: Macmillan, 1869), p. 82.
30. William Prout *et al.*, *Prout's Hypothesis, Alembic Club Reprints No. 20* (Edinburgh: Alembic Club, 1932), p. 47.

CHAPTER FIVE

1. Clara DeMilt, "Carl Weltzein and the Congress at Karlsruhe," *Chymia*, Vol. I (1948), p. 155.
2. John Dalton *et al.*, *Foundations of the Molecular Theory, Alembic Club Reprints No. 4* (Edinburgh: Alembic Club, 1899), pp. 8-9.
3. John Dalton, *A New System of Chemical Philosophy* (Manchester: R. Bickerstaff, Strand, London, 1808), Vol. I, p. 556.
4. Leicester and Klickstein, *op. cit.*, p. 232.
5. Conant, *op. cit.*, Vol. I, pp. 294-295.
6. DeMilt, *loc. cit.*, pp. 155, 163, 167.

7. Stanislao Cannizzaro, "Sketch of a Course of Chemical Philosophy," *Alembic Club Reprints No. 18* (Edinburgh: Alembic Club, 1910), pp. 2, 4-6, 42.
8. D. Mendeleeff, *The Principles of Chemistry*, trans. by George Kamensky (5th ed.; London: Longmans, Green, 1891), Vol. II, pp. 437, 439.
9. *Ibid.*, p. 436.
10. Ernst Mach, *Popular Scientific Lectures*, trans. by T. J. MacCormack (3rd ed.; Chicago: Open Court Publishing Co., 1898), p. 241.

CHAPTER SIX

1. *B.A.A.S. Fifth Report*, pp. 2, 6.
2. Grove, *op. cit.*, pp. 100-101.
3. *B.A.A.S. Fifth Report*, p. 5.
4. N. M. Ferrers, ed., *Mathematical Papers of the Late George Green* (London: Macmillan, 1871), p. 6.
5. Joseph Larmor, ed., *Origins of Clerk Maxwell's Electric Ideas as described in familiar letters to William Thomson* (Cambridge: University Press, 1937), pp. 7-8, 17.
6. Thompson, *op. cit.*, Vol. I, p. 83.
7. Thomson, *Electrostatics and Magnetism*, p. 1n.
8. Thomson, *Mathematical and Physical Papers*, Vol. I, p. 76.
9. Sir William Thomson, *Popular Lectures and Addresses* (2nd ed.; London: Macmillan, 1891), Vol. I, pp. 86-87.
10. Campbell and Garnett, *The Life of James Clerk Maxwell, with a Selection from his correspondence and Occasional Writings and a Sketch of his Contributions to Science* (London: Macmillan, 1882), p. 7n.
11. Larmor, *op. cit.*, pp. 28, 33.
12. James Clerk Maxwell, *A Treatise on Electricity and Magnetism* (3rd ed.; Dover Publications, 1954), pp. viii-ix.
13. Campbell and Garnett, *op. cit.*, p. 290.
14. Maxwell, *Treatise*, Vol. II, pp. 492-493.
15. *Ibid.*, pp. x-xi.
16. Larmor, *op. cit.*, pp. 17-18.
17. Nivens, *op. cit.*, Vol. I, pp. 155-156.
18. *Ibid.*, pp. 160, 159, 207, 187-188.
19. Larmor, *op. cit.*, p. 34.
20. Nivens, *op. cit.*, Vol. I, p. 452.
21. *Ibid.*, p. 486.

22. *Ibid.*, pp. 492, 500.
23. *Ibid.*, pp. 527, 542-543, 563-564.
24. Whittaker, *op. cit.*, Vol. I, p. 266.

CHAPTER SEVEN

1. Robert B. Lindsay, *The Role of Science in Civilization* (New York: Harper and Row, 1963), p. 35.
2. Thomas Young, "Outlines of Experiments and Inquiries respecting Sound and Light," in a letter to Edward Whitaker Gray, *Philosophical Transactions of the Royal Society of London* (1800), p. 106.
3. *Ibid.*, pp. 125-130.
4. *Dictionary of National Biography*, see Young.
5. Merz, *op. cit.*, Vol. II, pp. 16n-17n.
6. Henry Crew, ed., *The Wave Theory of Light* (New York: American Book, 1900), p. 47.
7. *Ibid.*, pp. 58-60.
8. Thomas Young, "On the Theory of Light and Colours," The Bakerian Lecture, Nov. 12, 1801, *Philosophical Transactions of the Royal Society of London* (1802), pp. 37, 35-36, 47, 48.
9. Merz, *op. cit.*, Vol. II, p. 17n.
10. Crew, *op. cit.*, pp. 68, 74.
11. *Edinburgh Review*, 7th ed., Vol. I, No. 2 (Jan., 1803), pp. 450-451.
12. *Dictionary of National Biography*, see Brougham.
13. Crew, *op. cit.*, p. 78.
14. Merz, *op. cit.*, Vol. II, p. 19n.
15. *Report of the Fourth Meeting of the British Association for the Advancement of Science*, held at Edinburgh in 1834 (London: John Murray, 1835), pp. 349-350.
16. Whewell, *op. cit.*, Vol. II, p. 473; and Merz, *op. cit.*, Vol. I, p. 241n.
17. Merz, *op. cit.*, Vol. I, pp. 241-242n.
18. *Ibid.*, Vol. II, p. 26n.
19. Whewell, *op. cit.*, Vol. II, pp. 474-475.
20. *Ibid.*, p. 468.
21. Merz, *op. cit.*, Vol. II, p. 9.
22. Crew, *op. cit.*, pp. 101n, 144, 81, 99.
23. Morris H. Shamos, *Great Experiments in Physics* (New York: Henry Holt, 1959), p. 114n.

24. François Arago, *Biographies of Distinguished Scientific Men,* trans. by Adm. W. H. Smyth, Rev. Baden Powell, and Robert Grant (London: Brown, Green, Longmanns and Roberts, 1857), see translator's note, pp. 426n-427n.

25. Whewell, *op. cit.,* Vol. II, pp. 464-466.

26. *B.A.A.S. Fourth Report,* pp. 349-350.

27. Poincaré, *op. cit.,* pp. 211, xxiv.

28. Pierre Duhem, *The Aim and Structure of Physical Theory* (Princeton: University Press, 1954), p. 103.

29. Merz, *op. cit.,* Vol. II, pp. 95-96.

30. Grove, *op. cit.,* p. 7.

CHAPTER EIGHT

1. Harry C. Jones, *A New Era in Chemistry, Some of the More Important Developments in General Chemistry during the Last Quarter of a Century* (New York: D. Van Nostrand, 1913), pp. 40, 38.

2. Meyer, *op. cit.,* p. 269.

3. *Ibid.,* pp. 268-269.

4. W. A. Shenstone, *Justus von Liebig, His Life and Work (1803-1873),* (London: Cassell, 1901), p. 201.

5. Meyer, *op. cit.,* p. 276n.

6. *Ibid.,* p. 274n.

7. *Ibid.,* p. 276.

8. Ernst von Meyer, *A History of Chemistry, From Earliest Times to the Present Day, Being Also an Introduction to the Study of the Science* (London: Macmillan, 1891), pp. 479-480.

9. *Report of the Twelfth Meeting of the British Association for the Advancement of Science,* held at Manchester in June, 1842 (London: John Murray, 1843), pp. 47-48.

10. Shenstone, *op. cit.,* pp. 140, 168, 71.

11. Wurtz, *op. cit.,* pp. 75-76.

12. Leicester and Klickstein, *op. cit.,* p. 346.

13. *Ibid.,* p. 353.

14. Wurtz, *op. cit.,* pp. 123-124.

15. Merz, *op. cit.,* Vol. I, pp. 413n-414n.

16. *Ibid.,* p. 421.

17. *Ibid.,* p. 415n.

18. Meyer, *op. cit.,* 3rd ed., pp. 340-341.

19. Mach, *op. cit.,* pp. 189-190, 222, 249-250, 207.

20. *The Scientific Papers of J. Willard Gibbs* (London: Longmans, Green, 1906), Vol. I, p. 32.

21. Eduard Farber, *The Evolution of Chemistry* (New York: Ronald Press, 1952), p. 215.

22. Lynde Phelps Wheeler, *Josiah Willard Gibbs, The History of a Great Mind* (New Haven: Yale University Press, 1951), pp. 88-89.

23. *Ibid.*, p. 151.

24. *Scientific Papers of Gibbs*, Vol. I, pp. xxiv-xxv.

25. Wheeler, *op. cit.*, pp. 151-152.

CHAPTER NINE

1. R. G. Collingwood, *The Idea of Nature* (Oxford: Clarendon Press, 1945), p. 1.

2. J. P. Joule, "Some Remarks on Heat and the Constitution of Elastic Fluids," *Philosophical Magazine,* Ser. 4, Vol. 14 (Sept., 1857), p. 214.

3. R. Clausius, "On the Nature of the Motion which we call Heat," *Philosophical Magazine,* Ser. 4, Vol. 14 (Aug., 1857), p. 108.

4. *Ibid.*, pp. 110-112.

5. R. Clausius, "On the Mean Length of the Paths described by the separate Molecules of Gaseous Bodies on the occurrence of Molecular Motion: together with some other Remarks upon the Mechanical Theory of Heat," *Philosophical Magazine,* Ser. 4, Vol. 17 (Feb., 1859), pp. 82-84, 90.

6. Nivens, *op. cit.*, Vol. II, p. 220.

7. *Ibid.*, Vol. I, pp. 377-378, 380, 391.

8. R. Clausius, "On the Conduction of Heat by Gases," *Philosophical Magazine,* Ser. 4, Vol. 23 (June, 1862), pp. 418n, 419-420, 428.

9. Nivens, *op. cit.*, Vol. II, p. 71.

10. *Ibid.*, p. 218.

11. *Ibid.*, p. 412

12. *Ibid.*, pp. 373-374.

13. Leonard B. Loeb, *Kinetic Theory of Gases* (1st ed.; New York: McGraw-Hill, 1927), p. 6.

14. *Ibid.*, p. 8.

15. Nivens, *op. cit.*, Vol. II, p. 372.

16. Thomson, *Popular Lectures*, Vol. I, pp. 235-236.

17. *Ibid.*, p. 240.

18. Nivens, *op. cit.*, Vol. II, p. 418.

CHAPTER TEN

1. Whittaker, *op. cit.*, Vol. I, p. 349.
2. M. Plucker, "Observations on the Electric Discharge," *Philosophical Magazine*, Ser. 4, Vol. 18 (July, 1859), p. 7.
3. M. Plucker, "On the Action of the Magnet upon the Electrical Discharge in Rarefied Gases," *Philosophical Magazine*, Ser. 4, Vol. 16 (July, 1858), pp. 119, 121, 409.
4. Magie, *op. cit.*, see selections from Crookes' papers; and *Philosophical Magazine*, Ser. 5, Vol. 7 (Jan., 1879), p. 57.
5. J. J. Thomson, "Cathode Rays," *Philosophical Magazine*, Ser. 5, Vol. 44 (Oct., 1897), p. 293.
6. Joseph Larmor, *Aether and Matter, A development of the Dynamical Relations of the Aether to Material Systems on the basis of the Atomic Constitution of Matter, including a discussion of the influence of the Earth's motion on optical phenomena* (Cambridge: University Press, 1900), p. 70.
7. Duhem, *op. cit.*, pp. 19, 21.
8. Heinrich Hertz, *Miscellaneous Papers*, trans. by D. E. Jones and G. A. Schott (London: Macmillan, 1896), pp. 245, 248, 253.
9. *Ibid.*, p. xxiii.
10. *Ibid.*, p. 328
11. J. J. Thomson, *Conduction of Electricity Through Gases* (Cambridge: University Press, 1903), p. 494.
12. J. J. Thomson, *Recollections and Reflections* (New York: Macmillan, 1937), p. 118.
13. J. J. Thomson, "On the Velocity of the Cathode Rays," *Philosophical Magazine*, Ser. 5, Vol. 38 (1894), p. 360.
14. Thomson, "Cathode Rays," pp. 293-296, 302, 310, 311.
15. George F. Fitzgerald, "Dissociation of Atoms," *The Electrician*, Vol. 39, (May, 1897), p. 104, c.2.

CHAPTER ELEVEN

1. William A. Tilden, "Mendeléef Memorial Lecture," *Memorial Lectures Delivered Before The Chemical Society 1901-1913* (London: Gurney and Jackson, 1914), p. 130.
2. F. A. Hayek, *The Counter-Revolution of Science* (Illinois: Free Press, 1952), p. 110.
3. Everett Mendelsohn, "The Emergence of Science as a Profession in Nineteenth-Century Europe," a chapter in *The Management of Scientists* (Beacon Press, 1964), pp. 11, 13.
4. Merz, *op cit.*, Vol. I, pp. 155-156.
5. *Ibid.*, pp. 215-216, 207n.

6. George Haines, *German Influence Upon English Education and Science, 1800-1866* (New London: Connecticut College, 1957), Monograph No. 6, pp. 31-32.
7. Merz, *op. cit.*, Vol. I, pp. 178n-179n, 190n.
8. Haines, *op. cit.*, pp. 48, 34-35.
9. *Ibid.*, pp. 55-56.
10. Friedrich Paulsen, *The German Universities and University Study*, trans. by Frank Thilly and William Elwang (New York: Charles Scribner's Sons, 1906), pp. 52-53.
11. *Ibid.*, pp. 408-409.
12. Merz, *op cit.*, Vol. I, pp. 168, 173.
13. Paulsen, *op. cit.*, pp. 63-66.
14. Merz, *op. cit.*, Vol. I, pp. 166-167.
15. *Ibid.*, p. 261n.
16. Thomas H. Huxley, *Science and Education Essays* (New York: D. Appleton, 1914), Vol. III, p. 255.
17. Merz, *op. cit.*, Vol. I, p. 254n.
18. Haines, *op. cit.*, pp. 13-14.
19. Thomson, *Recollections and Reflections*, pp. 136-137.
20. Haines, *op. cit.*, pp. 39n-40n.
21. Merz, *op. cit.*, Vol. I, pp. 286-287.
22. Haines, *op. cit.*, pp. 16-17.
23. Merz, *op. cit.*, Vol. I, pp. 273-274.
24. Haines, *op. cit.*, pp. 51-52.
25. Charles Babbage, *Reflections on the Decline of Science in England, and on Some of its Causes* (London: Printed for B. Fellows and J. Booth, 1830), pp. 24-25, 20-22.
26. Haines, *op. cit.*, p. 18.
27. Merz, *op. cit.*, Vol. I, p. 236n.
28. Babbage, *op. cit.*, pp. 141-142, 30-31, 52, 2.
29. Merz, *op. cit.*, Vol. I, p. 240.
30. Babbage, *op. cit.*, p. 214.
31. *Report of the First and Second Meetings of the British Association for the Advancement of Science*, held at York in 1831 and at Oxford in 1832 (London: John Murray, 1833), pp. iv, 9-10.
32. Babbage, *op cit.*, p. 126n.
33. *B.A.A.S. First and Second Report*, pp. 10, 11-12.
34. Merz, *op. cit.*, Vol. I, p. 240n.
35. *B.A.A.S. First and Second Report*, p. 16.
36. *Ibid.*, p. 107.

Bibliography

Arago, François, *Biographies of Distinguished Scientific Men,* trans. by
Adm. W. H. Smyth, Rev. Baden Powell, and Robert Grant.
London: Brown, Green, Longmanns and Roberts, 1857.

Babbage, Charles, *Reflections on the Decline of Science in England
and on Some of its Causes.* London: Printed for B.
Fellows and J. Booth, 1830.

Berthollet, C., "Researches respecting the Laws of Affinity," *Philosophical Magazine,* Vol. 9, 1801.

Berzelius, J. J., "Essay on the Cause of Chemical Proportions, and on
some circumstances relating to them: together with a short
and easy method of expressing them," *Annals of Philosophy,*
Vol. II, 1813.

_____ "An Address to those Chemists who wish to examine the
Laws of Chemical Proportions, and the Theory of Chemistry
in general," *Annals of Philosophy,* Vol. V, Jan.-June, 1815.

Campbell and Garnett, *The Life of James Clerk Maxwell, with a
Selection from his correspondence and Occasional Writings and
a Sketch of his Contributions to Science.* London: Macmillan,
1882.

Cannizzaro, Stanislao, "Sketch of a Course of Chemical Philosophy,"
Alembic Club Reprints No. 18. Edinburgh: Alembic Club,
1910.

Clausius, R., "On the Nature of the Motion which we call Heat," *Philosophical Magazine*, Ser. 4, Vol. 14, Aug., 1857.

———"On the Mean Length of the Paths described by the separate Molecules of Gaseous Bodies on the occurrence of Molecular Motion: together with some other Remarks upon the Mechanical Theory of Heat," *Philosophical Magazine*, Ser. 4, Vol. 17, Feb., 1859.

——— "On the Conduction of Heat by Gases," *Philosophical Magazine*, Ser. 4, Vol. 23, June, 1862.

Collingwood, R. G., *The Idea of Nature*. Oxford: Clarendon Press, 1945.

Conant, James Bryant, ed., *Harvard Case Studies in Experimental Science*. 2 vols. Cambridge: Harvard University Press, 1957.

Crew, Henry, ed., *The Wave Theory of Light*. New York: American Book, 1900.

Crowther, J. G., *British Scientists of the Nineteenth Century*. London: Kegan Paul, Trench, Trubner, 1935.

Dalton, John, *A New System of Chemical Philosophy*. 2 vols. Manchester: R. Bickerstaff, Strand, London, 1808-1827.

Dalton, John, *et al.*, *Foundations of the Molecular Theory, Alembic Club Reprints No. 4*. Edinburgh: Alembic Club, 1899.

——— *Foundations of the Atomic Theory, Alembic Club Reprints No. 2*. London: Gurney and Jackson, 1923.

Davy, Humphry, "The Bakerian Lecture, on some chemical Agencies of Electricity," *Philosophical Transactions of the Royal Society of London*, Vol. 97, 1807.

Davy, John, ed., *The Collected Works of Sir Humphry Davy, Bart.* 9 vols. London: Smith Elder, 1839-1840.

DeMilt, Clara, "Carl Weltzein and the Congress at Karlsruhe," *Chymia*, Vol. I, 1948.

Dibner, Bern, *Alessandro Volta and the Electric Battery*. New York: Franklin Watts, 1964.

Dictionary of National Biography.

Duhem, Pierre, *The Aim and Structure of Physical Theory*. Princeton: University Press, 1954.

Edinburgh Review, 7th ed., Vol. I, No. 2, Jan., 1803.

Ewart, Peter, "Observations on Mr. Dalton's Theory of Chemical Composition," *Annals of Philosophy*, Vol. VI, July-Dec., 1815.

Faraday, Michael, *Experimental Researches in Electricity*. 3 vols. London: Richard and John Edward Taylor, 1839-1855.

Farber, Eduard, *The Evolution of Chemistry*. New York: Ronald Press, 1952.

Ferrers, N. M., ed., *Mathematical Papers of the Late George Green*. London: Macmillan, 1871.

Fitzgerald, George F., "Dissociation of Atoms," *The Electrician*, Vol. 39, May, 1897.

Fleming, Sir John A., *The Alternate Current Transformer, In Theory and Practice*. 2 vols. New York: D. Van Nostrand, 1900.

Fourier, Joseph, *The Analytical Theory of Heat*, trans. by Alexander Freeman. Cambridge: University Press, 1878.

Grove, Sir William Robert, *et al.*, *The Correlation and Conservation of Forces: A Series of Expositions*. New York: D. Appleton, 1869.

Haines, George, *German Influence Upon English Education and Science, 1800-1866*. Monograph No. 6. New London: Connecticut College, 1957.

Hayek, F. A., *The Counter-Revolution of Science*. Illinois: Free Press, 1952.

Henry, William Charles, *Memoirs of the Life and Scientific Researches of John Dalton*. London: Printed for the Cavendish Society, 1854.

Hertz, Heinrich, *Miscellaneous Papers*, trans. by D. E. Jones and G. A. Schott. London: Macmillan, 1896.

Huxley, Thomas H., *Science and Education Essays*. New York: D. Appleton, 1914.

Jones, Harry C., *A New Era in Chemistry, Some of the More Important Developments in General Chemistry during the Last Quarter of a Century*. New York: D. Van Nostrand, 1913.

Joule, J. P., "Some Remarks on Heat and the Constitution of Elastic Fluids," *Philosophical Magazine*, Ser. 4. Vol. 14, Sept., 1857.

Larmor, Joseph, *Aether and Matter, A development of the Dynamical Relations of the Aether to Material Systems on the basis of the Atomic Constitution of Matter, including a discussion of the influence of the Earth's motion on optical phenomena*. Cambridge: University Press, 1900.

Larmor, Joseph, ed., *Origins of Clerk Maxwell's Electric Ideas as described in familiar letters to William Thomson*. Cambridge: University Press, 1937.

Leicester and Klickstein, *A Source Book in Chemistry 1400-1900*. New York: McGraw-Hill, 1952.

Lindsay, Robert B., *The Role of Science in Civilization*. New York: Harper and Row, 1963.

Loeb, Leonard B., *Kinetic Theory of Gases*. 1st ed. New York: McGraw-Hill, 1927.

Mach, Ernst, *Popular Scientific Lectures*, trans. by T. J. MacCormack. 3rd ed. Chicago: Open Court Publishing Co., 1898.

Magie, William F., *A Source Book in Physics*. 1st ed. New York: McGraw-Hill, 1935.

Maxwell, James Clerk, *Theory of Heat*. London: Longmans, Green, 1872.

————— *A Treatise on Electricity and Magnetism*. Republication of 3rd ed. of 1891, 2 vols. Dover Publications, 1954.

Mendeleeff, D., *The Principles of Chemistry*, trans. by George Kamensky. 5th ed., 2 vols. London: Longmans, Green, 1891.

Mendelsohn, Everett, "The Emergence of Science as a Profession in Nineteenth-Century Europe," in *The Management of Scientists*. Beacon Press, 1964.

Merz, John Theodore, *A History of European Thought in the Nineteenth Century*. 4 vols. London: William Blackwood and Sons, 1896-1914.

Meyer, Ernst von, *A History of Chemistry, From Earliest Times to the Present Day, Being Also an Introduction to the Study of the Science*. London: Macmillan, 1891, and 3rd ed., 1906.

Nivens, W. D., ed., *The Scientific Papers of James Clerk Maxwell*. 2 vols. Paris: Librairie Scientifique, 1927.

Paulsen, Friedrich, *The German Universities and University Study*, trans. by Frank Thilly and William Elwang. New York: Charles Scribner's Sons, 1906.

Philosophical Magazine, Ser. 5, Vol. 7, Jan., 1879.

Plücker, M., "On the Action of the Magnet upon the Electrical Discharge in Rarefied Gases," *Philosophical Magazine*, Ser. 4, Vol. 16, July, 1858.

————— "Observations on the Electric Discharge," *Philosophical Magazine*, Ser. 4, Vol. 18, July, 1859.

Poincaré, H., *Science and Hypothesis*. New York: Charles Scribner's Sons, 1907.

Prout, William, *et al.*, *Prout's Hypothesis, Alembic Club Reprints No. 20*. Edinburgh: Alembic Club, 1932.

Report of the First and Second Meetings of the British Association for the Advancement of Science, held at York in 1831 and at Oxford in 1832. London: John Murray, 1833.

Report of the Fourth Meeting of the British Association for the Advancement of Science, held at Edinburgh in 1834. London: John Murray, 1835.

Report of the Fifth Meeting of the British Association for the Advancement of Science, held at Dublin in 1835. London: John Murray, 1836.

Report of the Twelfth Meeting of the British Association for the Advancement of Science, held at Manchester in June, 1842. London: John Murray, 1843.

The Scientific Papers of J. Willard Gibbs. 2 vols. London: Longmans, Green, 1906.

The Scientific Papers of James Prescott Joule. 2 vols. Physical Society of London, 1884.

Shamos, Morris H., *Great Experiments in Physics.* New York: Henry Holt, 1959.

Shenstone, W. A., *Justus von Liebig, His Life and Work (1803-1873).* (The Century Series) London: Cassell, 1901.

Thompson, Silvanus P., *The Life of William Thomson, Baron Kelvin of Largs.* 2 vols. London: Macmillan, 1910.

Thomson, J. J., "On the Velocity of the Cathode Rays," *Philosophical Magazine,* Ser. 5, Vol. 38, 1894.

_____ "Cathode Rays," *Philosophical Magazine,* Ser. 5, Vol. 44, Oct., 1897.

_____ *Conduction of Electricity Through Gases.* Cambridge: University Press, 1903.

_____ *Recollections and Reflections.* New York: Macmillan, 1937.

Thomson, Sir William, *Mathematical and Physical Papers.* 6 vols. Cambridge: University Press. 1882.

_____ *Reprint of Papers on Electrostatics and Magnetism.* 2nd ed. London: Macmillan, 1884.

_____ *Popular Lectures and Addresses.* 2nd ed., 3 vols. London: Macmillan, 1891.

Tilden, William A., "Mendeléef Memorial Lecture," *Memorial Lectures Delivered Before The Chemical Society 1901-1913.* London: Gurney and Jackson, 1914.

Wheeler, Lynde Phelps, *Josiah Willard Gibbs, The History of a Great Mind.* New Haven: Yale University Press, 1951.

Whewell, William, *History of the Inductive Sciences, From the Earliest to the Present Times.* Rev. ed., 3 vols. London: John W. Parker, 1847.

Whittaker, Sir Edmund, *A History of the Theories of Aether and*

Electricity. 2 vols. New York: Philosophical Library, 1951, 1954.

Wurtz, Charles A., *The History of Chemical Theory, from the age of Lavoisier to the present time,* trans. and ed. by H. Watts. London: Macmillan, 1869.

Young, Thomas, "Outlines of Experiments and Inquiries respecting Sound and Light," *Philosophical Transactions of the Royal Society of London,* 1800.

————— "On the Theory of Light and Colours," The Bakerian Lecture, Nov. 12, 1801, *Philosophical Transactions of the Royal Society of London,* .1802.

Index